REVISE AQA GCSE (9–1)
Chemistry

REVISION WORKBOOK

Foundation

Series Consultant: Harry Smith

Author: Nora Henry

Also available to support your revision:

Revise GCSE Study Skills Guide   9781447967071

The **Revise GCSE Study Skills Guide** is full of tried-and-trusted hints and tips for how to learn more effectively. It gives you techniques to help you achieve your best – throughout your GCSE studies and beyond!

Revise GCSE Revision Planner   9781447967828

The **Revise GCSE Revision Planner** helps you to plan and organise your time, step by step, throughout your GCSE revision. Use this book and wall chart to mastermind your revision.

> **For the full range of Pearson revision titles across KS2, KS3, GCSE, Functional Skills, AS/A Level and BTEC visit:** www.pearsonschools.co.uk/revise

Contents

- - - - - - - - - - - - - -

A small bit of small print:
AQA publishes Sample Assessment Material and the Specification on its website. This is the official content and this book should be used in conjunction with it. The questions in this book have been written to help you practise every topic in the book. Remember: the real exam questions may not look like this.

Elements, mixtures and compounds

Question 1 is an example of a multiple-choice question, in which you only need to tick the correct answer. There will be many multiple-choice questions on both of your papers.

1 Which substance is an element?

Tick **one** box.

☐ air   ☐ iron sulfide

☐ copper   ☐ water   **(1 mark)**

2 The diagram shows particles present in three different substances. Circles represent atoms and different colours represent different elements.

A   B   C

(a) Which box, A, B or C, represents a mixture of different elements?   .... **(1 mark)**

(b) Which box, A, B or C, represents an element?   .... **(1 mark)**

3 What is a compound?

Tick **one** box.

☐ a substance made up of only one element

☐ a substance made up of two or more elements chemically joined together

☐ a substance made up of only metallic elements chemically joined together

☐ a substance made up of two or more elements physically mixed in a fixed ratio   **(1 mark)**

4 Some symbols and formulae are given in the box below.

NaOH	Al_2O_3	H_2O	Na	S	NH_3	CO

Write a formula or symbol from the box for:

(a) a metallic element   .... **(1 mark)**

(b) a compound containing four atoms   .... **(1 mark)**

(c) a compound containing three different elements   .... **(1 mark)**

5 When a mixture of the elements iron and sulfur is heated, a compound is formed.

(a) Name the compound formed.   .... **(1 mark)**

Guided

(b) Describe the difference between an element and a compound in terms of the atoms they contain.

An element contains one type of atom only. A compound ....

....

.... **(2 marks)**

Practical skills # Filtration, crystallisation and chromatography

1   The diagram shows some different apparatus used to separate mixtures.

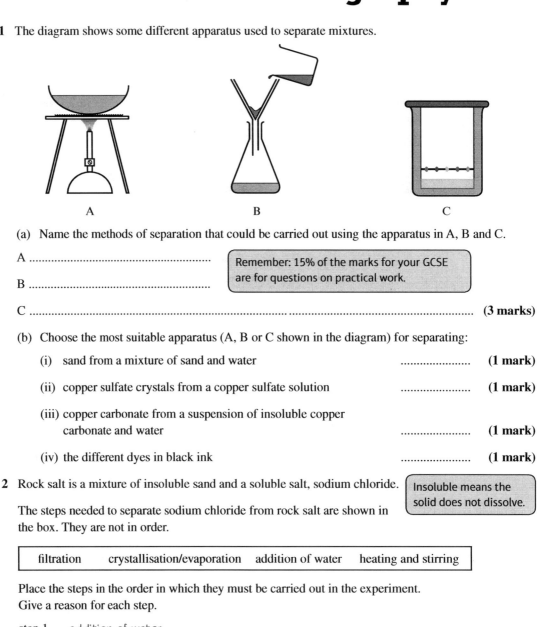

A   B   C

(a)   Name the methods of separation that could be carried out using the apparatus in A, B and C.

A ....

B ....

> Remember: 15% of the marks for your GCSE are for questions on practical work.

C .... **(3 marks)**

(b)   Choose the most suitable apparatus (A, B or C shown in the diagram) for separating:

   (i)   sand from a mixture of sand and water   .... **(1 mark)**

   (ii)   copper sulfate crystals from a copper sulfate solution   .... **(1 mark)**

   (iii)   copper carbonate from a suspension of insoluble copper
         carbonate and water   .... **(1 mark)**

   (iv)   the different dyes in black ink   .... **(1 mark)**

Guided

2   Rock salt is a mixture of insoluble sand and a soluble salt, sodium chloride.

> Insoluble means the solid does not dissolve.

The steps needed to separate sodium chloride from rock salt are shown in the box. They are not in order.

| filtration   crystallisation/evaporation   addition of water   heating and stirring |

Place the steps in the order in which they must be carried out in the experiment.
Give a reason for each step.

step 1   addition of water...

reason   to dissolve the sodium chloride ....

step 2   ....

reason   ....

step 3   ....

reason   ....

step 4   ....

reason   .... **(5 marks)**

Distillation

1 What is the best method to get water from a salt solution?

    Tick **one** box.

> Guided

| More than one of the methods can be used to obtain salt from a salt solution, but one method is much quicker than the others. |

☐ crystallisation   ☐ evaporation

☐ distillation   ☐ filtration   **(1 mark)**

2 Ethanol and water mix together completely. Ethanol and water have different boiling points.

    (a) What is the boiling point of water?

    .... **(1 mark)**

    (b) Name a method of separation used to
         separate a mixture of ethanol and water.

| Think about which method is used to separate a mixture of liquids. |

    .... **(1 mark)**

3 Two separation techniques are shown below. The diagrams are not labelled.

    (a) What is the name of the technique carried out using the apparatus on the left?

    .... **(1 mark)**

    (b) What is the purpose of the piece of apparatus labelled **A**?

    .... **(1 mark)**

    (c) What change of state happens at **B**?

    .... **(1 mark)**

    (d) No labels have been included in the diagrams.
         Name the labels that should be placed at:

| **Practical skills** It is important that you know how to label diagrams for all methods of separation. |

         C ....   **E** ....

         D ....

                                                                                      (3 marks)

    (e) Name a different way of heating the apparatus shown in the diagrams.

    .... **(1 mark)**   **3**

Historical models of the atom

1   The 'plum pudding' model of an atom, as shown below, suggested that the atom was a charged ball.

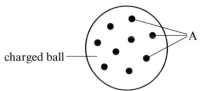

charged ball —

(a) What type of charge was thought to be on the ball in the plum pudding model?

.... **(1 mark)**

(b) Name particle A in the diagram.

.... **(1 mark)**

> **Guided**

(c) New evidence about atoms meant that the nuclear model has now replaced the plum pudding model. Describe the nuclear model of an atom.

The atom has a nucleus which contains ....

....

.... **(2 marks)**

2   The diagram shows Bohr's model of an atom.

(a) What is the name for the part of the atom labelled A?

.... **(1 mark)**

(b) What is the charge of the part of the atom labelled A?

.... **(1 mark)**

> Remember one particle had not been discovered at the time of Bohr's model.

(c) Name the type of particle found in A.

.... **(1 mark)**

(d) What is the name for the particle labelled B?

.... **(1 mark)**

3   Which scientist discovered the neutron?

Tick **one** box.

☐ Bohr   ☐ Einstein

☐ Chadwick   ☐ Rutherford   **(1 mark)**

Particles in an atom

1 (a) What is the symbol for the element calcium? Use the periodic table on page 116 to help you answer this question.

....

(1 mark)

  (b) What is the atomic number of calcium?

....

(1 mark)

2 An atom of sodium has an atomic number of 11 and a mass number of 23.

  (a) Define mass number.

....

(1 mark)

  (b) In terms of sub-atomic particles, why has a sodium atom no overall charge?

....

....

(1 mark)

  (c) Give the number of protons, neutrons and electrons in this atom of sodium.

      number of protons   ....

      number of neutrons   ....

      number of electrons   ....   **(3 marks)**

> Remember for an atom the number of protons equals the number of electrons.
> To find the number of neutrons subtract the atomic number from the mass number.

  (d) Name the two sub-atomic particles found in the nucleus of a sodium atom.

....

(1 mark)

3 (a) Complete the table below to give the number of protons, neutrons and electrons in each of four different atoms, A, B, C and D.

Atom	Atomic number	Mass number	Number of electrons	Number of neutrons	Number of protons
A	27	59	27	59 − 27 = 32	27
B	28	59			
C	13	27			
D	19	39			

(4 marks)

Guided

  (b) Use the periodic table on page 116 to give the name of each atom.

A *cobalt* ....

B ....

C ....

D ....

> The atomic number identifies an atom. For A the atomic number is 27, which is cobalt.

(4 marks)

Atomic structure and isotopes

1   An atom of potassium has the symbol $^{39}_{19}K$.

(a) Complete the table to show the relative mass and charge of each particle present in a potassium atom.

Particle	Relative mass	Relative charge
electron		
neutron		
proton		

(3 marks)

> Remember that number of protons = number of electrons. Remember also that number of neutrons = mass number minus atomic number.

(b) Give the number of protons, neutrons and electrons in this atom of potassium.

number of protons ....

number of neutrons ....

number of electrons ....   (3 marks)

(c) State the approximate radius of a potassium atom.

Give your answer in metres.

....   (1 mark)

(d) Another atom of potassium has the symbol $^{41}_{19}K$. Explain why atoms of $^{41}_{19}K$ and $^{39}_{19}K$ are isotopes.

....

....   (2 marks)

2   Carbon has two naturally occurring isotopes, ^{12}C and ^{13}C.

(a) Why are ^{12}C and ^{13}C isotopes?

Tick **one** box.

☐ They are atoms of the same element with a different number of electrons.

☐ They are atoms with the same atomic number and a different number of neutrons.

☐ They are atoms with a different atomic number and a different number of neutrons.

☐ They are atoms of the same element with a different number of protons.   (1 mark)

Guided

(b) Use the information about the two isotopes of carbon in the table below to calculate the relative atomic mass of carbon to one decimal place.

Mass number	12	13
Abundance	99	1

> **Maths skills** Remember, when rounding to one decimal place, if the second decimal place number is five or more, round up.

$$\text{relative atomic mass} = \frac{(\text{mass number isotope 1} \times \text{abundance}) + (\text{mass number isotope 2} \times \text{abundance})}{\text{total abundance}}$$

$$= \frac{(12 \times 99) + \text{......................}}{(99 + 1)} = \text{......................}$$ (2 marks)

Electronic structure

1   Which element has an electronic structure of 2,5?

Tick **one** box.

☐ oxygen   ☐ nitrogen   ☐ silicon   ☐ sulfur

(1 mark)

2   Complete the energy level (shell) diagrams for the elements with the following number of electrons.

Guided

13 electrons	17 electrons	20 electrons

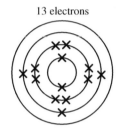 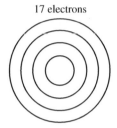 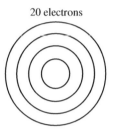

(3 marks)

3   Use the periodic table on page 116 to help you answer this question.

The diagram shows the electron structure of the atoms of an element.

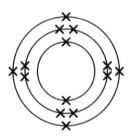

> To find the number of neutrons, you need to get the mass number from the periodic table and subtract the atomic number from it.

(a) What is the name and atomic number of this element?

.... **(2 marks)**

(b) State the number of protons and electrons in the atoms of this element.

.... **(1 mark)**

(c) What other information is needed to allow us to work out the number of neutrons in the nucleus of the atoms?

.... **(1 mark)**

4   The electronic structure of magnesium can be written as 2,8,2. Write the electronic structures for the following elements in the same way.

(a) potassium .... **(1 mark)**

(b) phosphorus .... **(1 mark)**

(c) calcium .... **(1 mark)**

Development of the periodic table

1   Below is part of Mendeleev's periodic table. Mendeleev left gaps in the table, marked by an asterisk (*).

H						
Li	Be	B	C	N	O	F
Na	Mg	Al	Si	P	S	Cl
K	Ca	*	Ti	V	Cr	Mn
Cu	Zn	*	*	As	Se	Br
Rb	Sr	Y	Zr	Nb	Mo	*
Ag	Cd	In	Sn	Sb	Te	I

(a) How many groups are in Mendeleev's periodic table?

.... **(1 mark)**

(b) Name a group in the modern periodic table which is not present in Mendeleev's periodic table.

.... **(1 mark)**

(c) State a difference between group 1 in Mendeleev's periodic table and group 1 in the modern periodic table.

.... **(1 mark)**

(d) State two differences between Mendeleev's periodic table and the modern periodic table.

....

.... **(2 marks)**

(e) The element in the fourth column marked by an asterisk (*) has the atomic number 32. Name this element.

> Each element in the periodic table has two numbers; the atomic number is the smaller one of the two. On the periodic table on page 116 find the element which has the atomic number 32.

.... **(1 mark)**

(f) Complete the sentence below by choosing the two most appropriate words from the list.

allotropes	isotopes	number	protons	mass	weight

The order of elements in Mendeleev's table is similar but not the same as in the modern periodic table.

> The modern periodic table is organised in order of atomic number.

Knowledge of .... made it

possible to explain why the order based on atomic .... was not

always correct. **(2 marks)**

2   Mendeleev listed the elements in his periodic table in an order. Which property did he use to list the elements?

Tick **one** box.

☐ atomic number   ☐ mass number

☐ atomic weight   ☐ number of neutrons   **(1 mark)**

The modern periodic table

1 The periodic table contains metals and non-metals.

(a) Classify the elements below as metals or non-metals.

barium ....

potassium ....

phosphorus .... **(3 marks)**

(b) Name a metal which is a liquid at room temperature.

.... **(1 mark)**

(c) Use the periodic table to help you complete the table.

Element	Group number	Number of electrons in outer shell
calcium		
fluorine		

(4 marks)

2 How are elements arranged in the modern periodic table?

Tick **one** box.

☐ by increasing atomic number   ☐ by increasing number of neutrons

☐ by increasing mass number   ☐ by increasing reactivity   **(1 mark)**

3 The diagram shows the position of six different elements in the periodic table. The letters do not represent the symbols for the elements.

Use the letters in the diagram to answer the questions below.

> Remember that metals are found on the left of the periodic table.

(a) Identify **two** metals with the same number of electrons in the outer shell of their atoms.

.... **(1 mark)**

(b) Identify a halogen.

.... **(1 mark)**

(c) Identify a non-metal that has five electrons in the outer shell of its atoms.

.... **(1 mark)**

4 Group 3 of the periodic table contains the elements boron, aluminium and gallium.

(a) Why do these three elements have similar chemical properties?

.... **(1 mark)**

Guided ▷ (b) Which of boron, aluminium and gallium has the lowest number of protons in the nucleus?

The element with the smallest atomic number is ....

The atomic number gives the number of protons, so the element with the lowest

number of protons is .... **(1 mark)**

Group 0

1 Neon is a noble gas. The atomic number of neon is 10.

(a) Write the electronic structure of neon.

.... **(1 mark)**

(b) Use your answer to (a) to explain why neon is unreactive.

.... **(1 mark)**

2 Which of the electronic structures below is the structure of an atom of a noble gas?

Tick **one** box.

☐ 2   ☐ 2,2   ☐ 2,8,2   ☐ 2,8,7   **(1 mark)**

3 The table below shows some properties of the noble gases.

Element	Boiling point in °C	Density in g/dm³	Relative atomic mass
helium	−269	0.2	4
neon	−246	0.9	20
argon	−190		40
krypton		3.8	84
xenon	−111	5.9	131

(a) What is the group number of the noble gases?

.... **(1 mark)**

(b) Predict the boiling point of krypton.

.... **(1 mark)**

(c) What is the relationship between boiling point and relative atomic mass?

....

.... **(1 mark)**

(d) Estimate the density of argon.

> Look at the general trend in density. You are asked for an estimate, so a value halfway between 0.9 and 3.8 is a good idea.

.... **(1 mark)**

(e) Write the electronic structures of helium and neon.

.... **(2 marks)**

4 Why do the atoms of noble gases not easily form molecules?

> Guided

Tick **one** box.

☐ ~~They all have 8 electrons in their outer shell.~~

☐ They have a full outer shell and are stable.

☐ They only form covalent bonds.

☐ Their reactivity decreases down the group.   **(1 mark)**

> The first answer in this guided question has been crossed out. This is because it is untrue – helium is a noble gas and it has only 2 electrons in its outer shell.

Group 1

1 Some of the elements of group 1 are listed below.

| lithium | sodium | potassium | rubidium |

(a) Which metal is the most reactive?

.... **(1 mark)**

(b) Which metal reacts with oxygen to give K_2O?

.... **(1 mark)**

(c) Which metal has the electronic structure 2,8,1?

.... **(1 mark)**

2 Two elements in group 1 of the periodic table are lithium and potassium.

(a) Explain why lithium and potassium are both in group 1 of the periodic table. Your answer should be in terms of their electronic structures.

....

.... **(1 mark)**

(b) Very small pieces of lithium and potassium are separately allowed to react with water.

(i) Describe the similarities and differences in what is observed.

....

....

....

....

....

.... **(4 marks)**

(ii) Name the products for the reaction of potassium with water.

.... **(2 marks)**

3 Sodium is a group 1 metal that reacts with non-metals.

(a) Complete the word equations for some reactions of sodium.

sodium + chlorine → ....

sodium + oxygen → .... **(2 marks)**

Guided (b) Sodium reacts with water to produce sodium hydroxide and hydrogen.

(i) Balance the equation for this reaction.

............Na + ...H_2O → ..2NaOH + H_2 **(1 mark)**

(ii) Name the ion which makes the final solution alkaline.

.... **(1 mark)**

> First a 2 is placed in front of the NaOH. Now there are two oxygens on the right of the equation. Balance the oxygen on the left – you must put a number in front of the H_2O. Then balance the Na.

Group 7

1 What is the name for group 7 in the periodic table?

Tick **one** box.

☐ alkali metals   ☐ noble gases

☐ halogens   ☐ transition metals   **(1 mark)**

2 Group 7 elements react with group 1 metals such as sodium and potassium.

(a) Write a word equation for the reaction of sodium with bromine.

.... **(1 mark)**

(b) How many electrons are in the outer shell of bromine?

> Remember, you do not need to the write electronic structure for this –
> the group number is all that you need.

.... **(1 mark)**

(c) Balance the equation for the reaction of potassium with chlorine.

.... $K + Cl_2 \rightarrow$ .... KCl **(1 mark)**

(d) Name the product KCl.

.... **(1 mark)**

3 The table shows the results of adding halogens to solutions of halide ions.

Halogen	Sodium chloride solution	Sodium bromide solution	Sodium iodide solution
chlorine		orange solution produced	brown solution produced
bromine	no reaction		brown solution produced
iodine	no reaction	no reaction	

⟩ **Guided** ⟩   (a) Explain why there is no reaction between sodium chloride and bromine.

Reactivity decreases down the group and so bromine is less reactive than ....

....

.... **(2 marks)**

(b) Complete the word equation for the reaction between chlorine and sodium iodide.

chlorine + sodium iodide → .... **(1 mark)**

(c) State the name of the type of reaction in (b).

.... **(1 mark)**

(d) What does the information in the table show about the trend in reactivity of the halogens?

....

.... **(1 mark)**

Transition metals

1 Which element is a transition metal?

Tick **one** box.

☐ aluminium   ☐ chromium

☐ calcium   ☐ lead   **(1 mark)**

2 Iron is used as a catalyst in the production of ammonia. Iron can form iron(II) ions (Fe^{2+}) and iron(III) ions (Fe^{3+}). Both of these ions have different colours in solution.

> **Guided**

   (a) State three pieces of information that show that iron is a transition metal.

Like all transition metals iron is a catalyst, ...

....

.... **(3 marks)**

   (b) Work out the formula of iron(II) oxide and iron(III) oxide.

> Oxide ions have the formula O^{2-}.

iron(II) oxide ....

iron(III) oxide .... **(2 marks)**

3 Tick (✓) true or false for each of the following general statements comparing the properties of transition metals with alkali metals.

Statements	True	False
Alkali metals have higher densities than transition metals.		
Transition metals are stronger than alkali metals.		
Alkali metals are harder than transition metals.		
Transition metals are more reactive than alkali metals.		

(4 marks)

4 This question refers to the elements in the different blocks of the periodic table shown below.

Which of the blocks A to E contain:

(a) mostly non-metals? .... **(1 mark)**

(b) the group of elements that usually form ions with a 1+ charge? .... **(1 mark)**

(c) metals that are often used as catalysts? .... **(1 mark)**

(d) the most unreactive elements? .... **(1 mark)**

Chemical equations

1   Complete the word equations.

   (a) potassium + chlorine → ....

   (b) magnesium + oxygen → ....

   (c) hydrogen + bromine → ....

   (d) copper + oxygen → .... **(4 marks)**

2   The chemical equation for the reaction between methane and oxygen is shown below.

> **Guided**

   $CH_4 + 2O_2 \rightarrow CO_2 + 2H_2O$

   (a) Describe this reaction between methane and oxygen in terms of the names of the substances and the number of molecules involved.

   One molecule of methane reacts ....

   .... **(2 marks)**

   (b) When 4 g of methane burns, 11 g of carbon dioxide and 9 g of water are produced.

   What mass of oxygen was needed to react with the 4 g of methane?

   mass of products = 11 + 9

   = 20 g

   mass of oxygen   = ... g

   > Remember: no atoms are gained or lost during a chemical reaction, so the total mass of reactants used up will always equal the total mass of products formed.

   (1 mark)

3   Balance the following equations.

   (a) ..... Mg + ... O_2 → ..... MgO   **(1 mark)**

   (b) ..... HCl + ... Ca → ..... $CaCl_2$ + ... H_2 **(1 mark)**

   (c) ..... N_2 + ... H_2 → ..... NH_3 **(1 mark)**

   (d) ..... SO_2 + ... O_2 → ..... SO_3 **(1 mark)**

   (e) ..... H_2 + ... F_2 → ..... HF   **(1 mark)**

4   Sodium metal burns in oxygen to form sodium oxide.

   .... Na + O_2 → .... Na_2O

   (a) Balance the above symbol equation for the reaction of sodium and oxygen.   **(2 marks)**

   (b) Potassium burns in oxygen in a similar way to sodium.

   > Remember that oxygen is diatomic. Work out the formula of potassium oxide first.

   Write a balanced symbol equation for the reaction of potassium and oxygen.

   .... **(2 marks)**

5   $C_2H_5OH + yO_2 \rightarrow 2CO_2 + 3H_2O$

   What is the value of y in the equation above?

   Tick **one** box.

   ☐ 2   ☐ 3   ☐ 3½   ☐ 6   **(1 mark)**

Extended response – Atomic structure

Compare the chemical and physical properties of the alkali metals with those of the transition metals.

> The question asks you to compare, so make sure you do this, by considering properties that are the same and properties that are different. In your answers, use statements like 'The alkali metals …, but the transition metals…'. Try to compare chemical properties such as reactions with water, and the charges on the ions formed, and physical properties such as melting point, hardness and density.

....

....

....

....

....

....

....

....

....

....

....

....

....

....

....

....

....

....

....

....

....

.... (6 marks)

> Check your answer and make sure you have fully answered the question. It is a good idea to tick the parts of the question you have done, so you do not leave points out.

Forming bonds

1 What holds the ions in sodium chloride together?

   Tick **one** box.

   ☐ covalent bonds   ☐ metallic bonds

   ☑ electrostatic forces   ☐ magnetic forces   **(1 mark)**

2 (a) Complete the table by inserting each of the elements listed below into the correct column.

Guided

   | chlorine   oxygen   hydrogen   calcium   magnesium   sulfur   nitrogen |

Metal	Non-metal
magnesium calcium	chlorine oxygen nitrogen sulfur hydrogen

   Find chlorine on the periodic table on page 116 – it is on the right of the periodic table so it is a non-metal. Now find oxygen on the periodic table.

                                                                         (2 marks)

   Ionic bonding occurs in compounds formed from metals combined with non-metals.
   Covalent bonding occurs in most non-metal elements and compounds.

   (b) Complete the table by ticking (✓) the correct type of bonding in the compound.

Compound	Ionic bonding	Covalent bonding
calcium oxide	✓	
hydrogen chloride		✓
hydrogen sulfide		✓
magnesium chloride	✓	

                                                                         (4 marks)

3 The diagram shows the bonding in a compound of nitrogen and hydrogen.

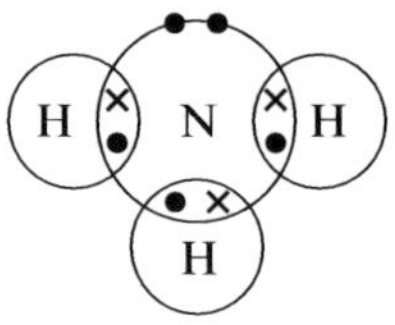

   (a) Write the formula of the compound shown in the diagram.

   ....H₃N..

                                                                         (1 mark)

   (b) Name and describe the type of bonding shown in the diagram.

   ....covalent since.......between two non metals....

   ....The bonding is.................................... **(2 marks)**

   (c) What type of bonding is represented in the diagram to the right?

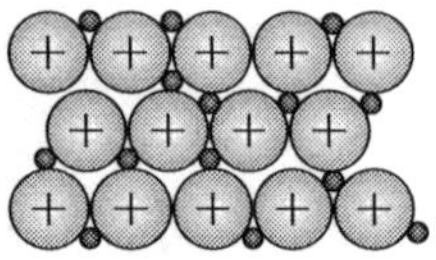

   ....Metalic..

                                                                         (1 mark)

4 Which pair of elements forms a covalent compound?

   Tick **one** box.

   ☐ lithium and chlorine   ☑ nitrogen and hydrogen

   ☐ magnesium and oxygen   ☐ potassium and bromine   **(1 mark)**

Ionic bonding

1   What is the charge on an oxide ion?

> Oxygen has atomic number 8 so its electronic structure is 2,6. Now work out how many electrons it needs to lose or gain to obtain a full outer shell.

Tick **one** box.

☐ 1–   ☑ 2–

☐ 1+   ☐ 2+   **(1 mark)**

2   (a) Write the electronic structure of a sodium atom.

......................2,8,1......................   **(1 mark)**

(b) Write the electronic structure of a sodium ion.

......................2,8......................   **(1 mark)**

3   What happens when calcium reacts with chlorine to form calcium chloride?

Tick **one** box.

☐ Each chlorine atom loses one electron.

☐ Each chlorine atom gains one electron.

☑ Each calcium atom gains one electron.

☐ Each calcium atom gains two electrons.   **(1 mark)**

4   Sodium forms an ionic compound with oxygen. Describe what happens when two atoms of sodium react with one atom of oxygen. Give the formulae of the ions formed.

Guided

> You need to work out the number of electrons in the outer shell of each atom, and think about their transfer, as shown in the diagram. Then describe in words where the electrons transfer from and to, and how many electrons are involved.

Two sodium atoms each lose ...1 electron which gets transferred over to the oxygen atom which needs two electrons to form a oxide ion......................

....

....

....

....

....

....

....

....   **(5 marks)**

Giant ionic lattices

1   Sodium chloride is an ionic compound. Tick (✓) two properties of ionic compounds.

Property	Tick
usually dissolve in water	
high melting point	
low boiling point	
never conduct electricity	

(2 marks)

2   What surrounds each sodium ion in a sodium chloride crystal?

Tick **one** box.

☐ one chloride ion

☐ two chloride ions

☐ four chloride ions

☐ six chloride ions

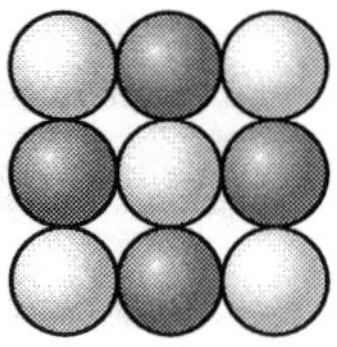

(1 mark)

3   The structure of caesium chloride can be represented using the ball-and-stick model shown in the diagram.

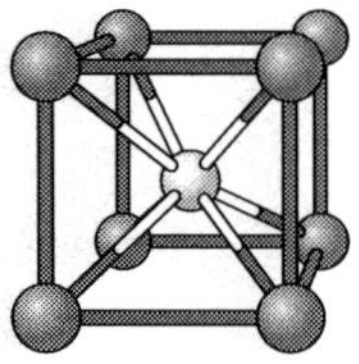

(a)   What type of bonding is found in caesium chloride?

....   **(1 mark)**

(b)   What is the name for this type of structure?

....   **(1 mark)**

(c)   The ball-and-stick model is not a good representation of an ionic compound.

Give one reason why. | Think about how the ions fit together in the crystal. |

....

....   **(1 mark)**

(d)   What holds the ions together in caesium chloride?

....

....   **(2 marks)**

Guided   (e)   Why does calcium chloride solid not conduct electricity?

The ions are held tightly in the ....

....   **(2 marks)**

18

Covalent bonding

1   The dot-and-cross diagrams of some molecules are shown below.

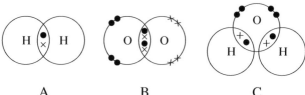

        A   B   C

(a)   Which substance, A, B or C, contains a double covalent bond?

.... **(1 mark)**

(b)   Which substance, A, B or C, contains no lone pairs?

.... **(1 mark)**

(c)   Which substance, A, B or C, contains two lone pairs?

.... **(1 mark)**

(d)   What is the name of substance C?

.... **(1 mark)**

2   Complete the dot-and-cross diagram to show the bonding in a molecule of hydrogen chloride. Show the outer shell electrons only.

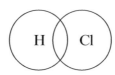

                                                      (2 marks)

3   A dot-and-cross diagram for the bonding in a molecule of the gas phosphine is shown below.

> Remember that a lone pair is an unbonded pair of electrons and a covalent bond is a shared pair of electrons.

   (a)   Complete the diagram by labelling:

       (i)   a lone pair   **(1 mark)**

       (ii)   a covalent bond.   **(1 mark)**

   (b)   Give the formula of phosphine.

.... **(1 mark)**

   (c)   Is phosphine a compound or an element?

.... **(1 mark)**

   (d)   What is a covalent bond?

.... **(1 mark)**

Small molecules

1 Phosphine (PH_3) is a gas made of small molecules.

(a) Name the type of bonding in phosphine.

.... **(1 mark)**

(b) Explain if phosphine conducts electricity.

> To conduct electricity, free electrons or ions are needed to carry the charge. Are there any in phosphine?

....

.... **(2 marks)**

2 The molecules of two chlorine compounds are shown below.

A   B

(a) Write the molecular formula of the compound shown in:

(i) A .... **(1 mark)**

(ii) B .... **(1 mark)**

(b) Draw a diagram of the compound in diagram A above. Use letters to represent the atoms and a line to represent each single bond.

(1 mark)

3 Complete the dot and cross diagram to represent the compound ammonia NH_3. Show outer electrons only and the hydrogen electrons as crosses.

> Nitrogen has atomic number 7 and electronic structure 2,5. The 5 outer electrons of nitrogen are shown. Hydrogen has atomic number 1 and electronic structure 1. To complete NH_3, use the outer electron on each of the 3 hydrogen atoms so that nitrogen has a full outer shell of 8 electrons.

•N•

(1 mark)

4 Why does hydrogen chloride have a low boiling point?

Tick **one** box.

☐ It is covalently bonded.   ☐ The covalent bonds between the atoms are weak.

☐ It is ionically bonded.   ☐ The forces between the molecules are weak.   **(1 mark)**

Polymer molecules

1 (a) What is a polymer?

....

.... **(1 mark)**

(b) Name the elements present in the polymer shown in the diagram above.

.... **(2 marks)**

(c) What type of bonding is present between the atoms in the polymer shown in the diagram above?

.... **(1 mark)**

2 Draw the bonds to complete the displayed formula of the polymer PVC shown in the diagram below.

> Remember that this is just the repeating unit and the bonds need to go through the brackets to represent this.

$$\left[\begin{array}{cc} H & H \\ | & | \\ C & C \\ | & | \\ H & Cl \end{array}\right]_n$$

(1 mark)

> **Guided**

3 Circle the correct word to complete the sentences below.

Polymers have very **large**/small molecules.

The **atoms/ions** in the polymer molecules are linked to others by **strong/weak** covalent bonds.

The intermolecular forces between polymer molecules are relatively **strong/weak** and so these substances are solids at room temperature.

(4 marks)

4 The structure of poly(ethene) is represented in the diagram.

$$\left[\begin{array}{cc} H & H \\ | & | \\ C & C \\ | & | \\ H & H \end{array}\right]_n \xleftarrow{\hspace{1em}} B$$

(a) What does *n* represent?

.... **(1 mark)**

(b) What label should be placed at B?

.... **(1 mark)**

(c) In what physical state does this polymer exist at room temperature and pressure?

.... **(1 mark)**

Diamond and graphite

1   The diagram shows the structure of an element.
    What is the name of this element?

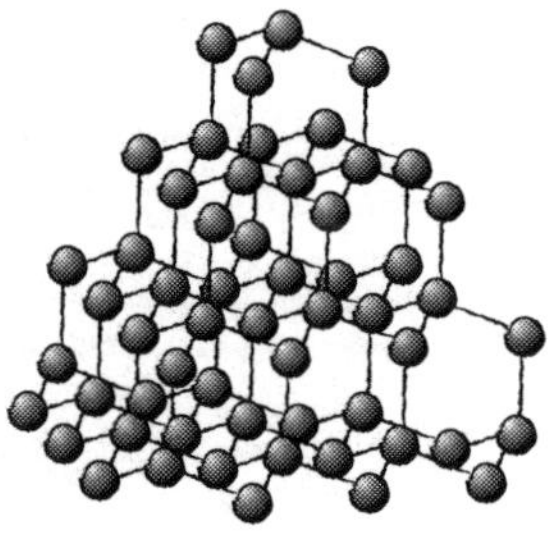

    Tick **one** box.

    ☐ argon   ☐ carbon

    ☐ calcium   ☐ silver

    (1 mark)

2   Why does the element in the diagram for question **1** not conduct electricity?

    Tick **one** box.

    ☐ It has covalent bonds.   ☐ It has ionic bonds.

    ☐ It has no free electrons or ions.   ☐ It has a rigid shape.   **(1 mark)**

3   Many substances have giant covalent structures or simple molecular structures.

    Choose the correct structure, giant covalent or simple molecular, for each of the
    following substances.

    > Your specification only expects you to know of three giant
    > covalent structures: graphite, diamond and silicon dioxide.

    ammonia ....

    carbon dioxide ....

    diamond ....

    silicon dioxide ....

    water ....   **(5 marks)**

Guided

4   The diagram shows the structure of graphite.
    Complete the diagram by inserting the correct labels in each box.

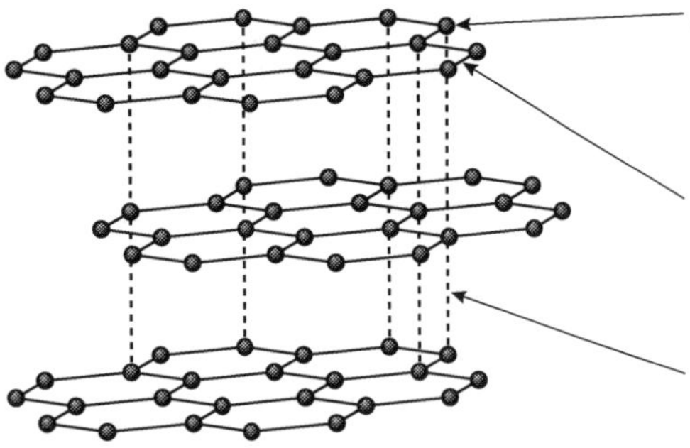

    A ....

    B ....

    C intermolecular force ....

    (3 marks)

Graphene and fullerenes

1 Tick (✓) two correct statements about graphene.

Statement	Tick (✓)
Graphene is a cylindrical fullerene.	
Graphene is a single layer of graphite.	
Graphene has rings of five carbon atoms.	
Graphene has hexagonal rings of carbon.	

(2 marks)

2 Which structure is shown in the diagram?

each carbon atom joined to three others

strong covalent bond

Tick **one** box.

☐ buckminsterfullerene   ☐ graphene

☐ diamond   ☐ graphite   **(1 mark)**

3 Fullerenes are molecules of carbon atoms with hollow shapes. The structure of fullerenes is based on rings of carbon atoms.

(a) How many carbon atoms do most rings of a fullerene contain? Choose **two** numbers from the box.

4	5	6	7	8	20	60

(1 mark)

Guided

(b) Name two fullerenes.

carbon nanotubes and .... **(2 marks)**

4 The figure shows the structure of a type of cylindrical fullerene.

(a) Name this type of fullerene.

.... **(1 mark)**

Guided

(b) State two physical properties of the cylindrical fullerene in the figure.

This fullerene is a .... conductor of electricity and has a .... tensile strength.

(2 marks)

> To successfully answer questions on this topic you need to remember that the molecules are all made of carbon and try to remember their shapes – graphene (layer), fullerene (sphere) and nanotubes (cylinder).

Metallic bonding

1 (a) In which way are the atoms arranged in a metal?

Tick **one** box.

☐ in a sphere   ☐ in a hexagon shape

☐ in layers   ☐ in a tetrahedral arrangement   **(1 mark)**

(b) The electrons in the outer shell of metal atoms are free to move through the whole structure.
What term is used to describe this?

.... **(1 mark)**

2 The diagram shows the structure of the metal sodium.

(a) Describe the structure of the metal sodium.

....

....

.... **(2 marks)**

(b) What is a metallic bond?

....

....

.... **(2 marks)**

3 The table below gives some properties of the metal calcium and one of its compounds, calcium chloride.

Property	Calcium	Calcium chloride
Melting point in °C	842	772
Electrical conductivity when solid	conducts	does not conduct
Electrical conductivity when molten	conducts	conducts

Remember there are three types of strong bonding – metallic, ionic and covalent.

(a) Name the type of bonding found in:

(i)   calcium .... **(1 mark)**

(ii) calcium chloride .... **(1 mark)**

(b) Apart from its melting point and electrical conductivity, suggest one other physical property of calcium.

.... **(1 mark)**

Giant metallic structures and alloys

1 Gold (Au) is the most malleable metal.

(a) (i) What does **malleable** mean?

Tick **one** box.

☐ can be drawn into a wire ☐ can conduct electricity

☐ can be hammered into shape ☐ is shiny **(1 mark)**

(ii) Why can gold conduct electricity?

Tick **one** box.

☐ It contains ions which can move. ☐ It contains delocalised electrons.

☐ It has covalent bonding. ☐ It has layers of atoms. **(1 mark)**

Guided

(iii) Give the name and the number present of each particle found in the nucleus of a gold atom. You may find the periodic table on page 116 useful.

> The number of protons equals the number of electrons in an atom, and equals the atomic number.

protons ....

> The mass number minus the atomic number equals the number of neutrons.

.... **(2 marks)**

(b) Pure gold is very soft. It is often alloyed with other metals, such as copper or silver, for use in jewellery.

Explain, in terms of its structure, why an alloy is harder than a pure metal.

....
....
.... **(2 marks)**

2 The figure shows an alloy made of metals A and B.

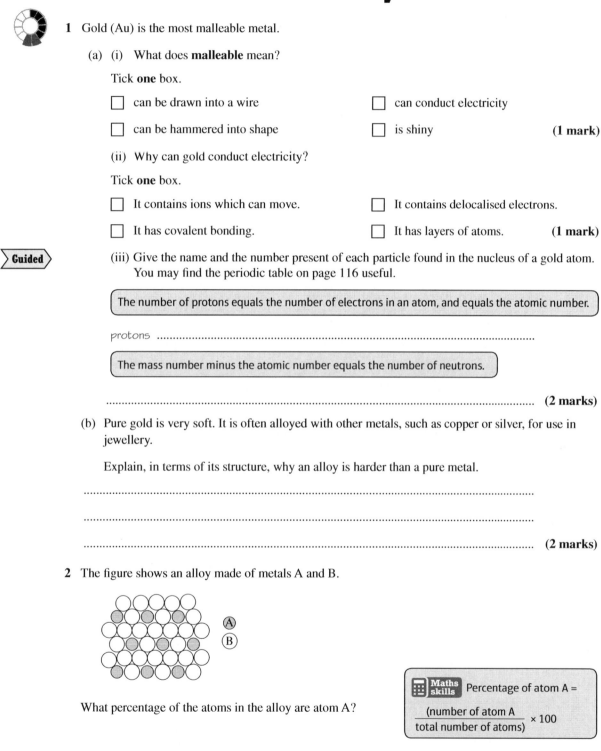

What percentage of the atoms in the alloy are atom A?

> **Maths skills** Percentage of atom A =
> $\frac{\text{(number of atom A)}}{\text{total number of atoms)}} \times 100$

.... **(2 marks)**

The three states of matter

> Melting point is the temperature at which a solid changes to a liquid, and boiling point is the temperature at which a liquid changes to a gas.

1 The table below shows the melting point and boiling point of four substances, A, B, C and D.

Substance	Melting point in °C	Boiling point in °C
W	–95	9
X	325	1755
Y	800	1412
Z	–38	356

What state is each of the substances in at room temperature (20 °C)?

W ....

X ....

Y ....

Z .... **(4 marks)**

2 The diagram shows the arrangement of particles in a solid, in a liquid and in a gas.

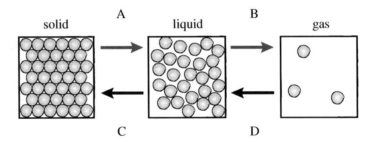

Guided   (a) Name each change of state, A, B, C and D.

A melting   ..

B ....

C ....

D .... **(4 marks)**

(b) Describe what happens to the movement and arrangement of the particles when the solid is heated until it changes to a liquid.

....

....

.... **(2 marks)**

Nanoscience

1   Which answer gives the correct order of increasing size?

Tick **one** box.

☐ atom, nanoparticle, fine particle, coarse particle

☐ nanoparticle, atom, fine particle, coarse particle

☐ nanoparticle, fine particle, coarse particle, atom

☐ fine particle, coarse particle, nanoparticle, atom   **(1 mark)**

2   Nanoscience is a branch of research into the properties of nanoparticles, which have applications in a number of different areas.

> In your answer refer to the size of the particle.

(a) What is a nanoparticle?

....

.... **(1 mark)**

▷ **Guided** ▷   (b) Describe how the surface area of nanoparticles compares with that of ordinary powder particles.

Compared with the particles in ordinary powders, nanoparticles have a surface area that

is very .... **(1 mark)**

3   Read the information in the box and then answer the questions.

Nanotechnology, good or bad?

Nanoparticles have been developed with many interesting new properties, and these are used in sunscreens, drug delivery, catalysts and computing. However, some scientists are concerned about the introduction of new nanotechnology. As they are so small, nanoparticles can get everywhere and can be absorbed into any part of the human body. Their full effects are unpredictable as we don't yet know all their properties. For example, silver nanoparticles, which can be used in place of antibiotics to kill bacteria, might damage other cells in different parts of the body. We therefore have to do more research, and control the trials and use of this new technology very carefully.

(a) Why are nanoparticles potentially so useful?

....

....

.... **(2 marks)**

(b) What general property of nanoparticles would make them useful as catalysts?

.... **(1 mark)**

(c) Why do we have to control the introduction of nanotechnology?

.... **(1 mark)**

Extended response – Bonding and structure

Copper is a transition metal. Some of the physical properties of copper are shown in the table below.

Physical properties of copper
high melting point
good conductor of electricity
good conductor of heat
soft and malleable

Explain, in terms of structure and bonding, the physical properties of copper.

> Before you begin, think about the type of bonding present in copper and the type of particles that make up the structure. Make sure you use the correct terminology in your answer.

....

....

....

....

....

....

....

....

....

....

....

....

....

....

....

....

....

....

.... **(6 marks)**

> When you have finished your answer, read it through and tick each of the physical properties you have explained to ensure you have not left any out.

Relative formula mass

Use the periodic table on page 116 to help answer the following questions.

> You need to look up the relative atomic mass of each element in the periodic table – it is the larger of the two numbers.

1 Calculate the relative formula mass of each substance in the table.

Substance	Relative formula mass
Cl_2	
HF	
NaOH	
K_2O	

(4 marks)

2 Calculate the relative formula mass (M_r) of the following:

Guided

(a) sodium oxide, Na_2O

Na_2O

$\downarrow$ 1 × 16 = 16

$\downarrow$ 2 × 23 = ...

M_r = ... (1 mark)

(b) sucrose, molecular formula = $C_{12}H_{22}O_{11}$

M_r = ... (1 mark)

(c) ethyl ethanoate, structural formula =

$$H-\overset{\overset{\displaystyle H}{|}}{\underset{\underset{\displaystyle H}{|}}{C}}-\overset{\overset{\displaystyle O}{\|}}{C}-O-\overset{\overset{\displaystyle H}{|}}{\underset{\underset{\displaystyle H}{|}}{C}}-\overset{\overset{\displaystyle H}{|}}{\underset{\underset{\displaystyle H}{|}}{C}}-H$$

M_r = ... (1 mark)

(d) sulfuric acid, H_2SO_4

M_r = ... (1 mark)

(e) calcium nitrate, $Ca(NO_3)_2$

> **Maths skills** Remember that brackets mean you multiply everything inside the brackets by the number outside – there are 2 N atoms and 6 O atoms.

M_r = ... (1 mark)

(f) aluminium sulfate, $Al_2(SO_4)_3$

M_r = ... (1 mark)

Balanced equations and masses

1 An antacid tablet for indigestion contains sodium hydrogen carbonate and citric acid. When added to water the tablet fizzes as the sodium hydrogen carbonate reacts with the citric acid to produce a salt, called a citrate.

   (a) (i) Complete the word equation for the formation of a salt, carbon dioxide and water from citric acid:

> Remember to name the salt.

          sodium hydrogen carbonate + citric acid →

          .... + ... + ... **(1 mark)**

      (ii) Use the equation in (a)(i) to explain what causes the fizz.

      .... **(1 mark)**

   (b) In an experiment an antacid tablet is added to $50\,cm^3$ of water in a conical flask. The flask is loosely stoppered with a cotton-wool plug and placed on a balance. The initial reading is $103.261\,g$.

> **Guided**

      (i) Draw a labelled diagram of the apparatus.

> The balance has been drawn for you. Read the description and think of the other things you need to draw.

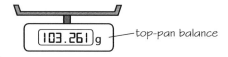
top-pan balance

                                                                         (3 marks)

      (ii) Why did the balance reading decrease?

      Tick **one** box.

      ☐ **A** The tablet broke down.   ☐ **C** A gas was lost from the flask.

      ☐ **B** A salt was produced in the reaction.   ☐ **D** Water was produced in the reaction.

                                                                                    (1 mark)

2 Copper carbonate and hydrochloric acid react as shown in the equation:

$$CuCO_3 + 2HCl \rightarrow CuCl_2 + H_2O + CO_2$$

   (a) Complete the table.

Reactant	Relative formula mass	Product	Relative formula mass
$CuCO_3$		$CuCl_2$	
HCl		H_2O	
		CO_2	

                                                                                 (5 marks)

> **Guided**

   (b) Use your calculated values in (a) to show that the equation for the reaction is balanced.

> **Maths skills** Remember that 2 moles of HCl are used so $2 \times Mr$ is needed.

     total formula mass of reactants =..

     .... **(2 marks)**

Concentration of a solution

1 Sea water contains dissolved salts.

Which row (**A**, **B**, **C** or **D**) correctly describes the components of sea water?

	Solute	Solvent	Solution
☐ **A**	water	salt	sea water
☐ **B**	salt	sea water	water
☐ **C**	sea water	salt	water
☐ **D**	salt	water	sea water

(1 mark)

Guided

2 Calculate the following volumes in dm^3.

> **Maths skills** $1\,dm^3 = 1000\,cm^3$.

(a) $2500\,cm^3$

$$volume = \frac{2500}{1000} = \text{.............} \; dm^3$$ **(1 mark)**

(b) $500\,cm^3$

.... **(1 mark)**

(c) $25\,cm^3$

.... **(1 mark)**

3 Calculate the concentrations of the following solutions in g/dm^3:

(a) 50 g of sodium hydroxide dissolved in $2\,dm^3$ of water

.... **(1 mark)**

(b) 14.6 g of hydrogen chloride dissolved in $0.400\,dm^3$ of water

.... **(1 mark)**

(c) 0.25 g of glucose dissolved in $0.050\,dm^3$ of water.

.... **(1 mark)**

Guided

4 A student dissolves 10 g of copper sulfate in $250\,cm^3$ of water. Calculate the concentration of the solution formed in g/dm^3:

$$concentration = \left(\frac{10}{250}\right) \times 1000 = \text{....................................}$$ **(1 mark)**

5 A student dissolves 2.0 g of silver nitrate in $125\,cm^3$ of water. Calculate the concentration of the solution formed in g/dm^3:

.... **(1 mark)**

6 A school technician wants to make $2.5\,dm^3$ of a $40\,g/dm^3$ aqueous solution of sodium hydroxide.

(a) Describe the meaning of the term '**aqueous solution**'.

.... **(1 mark)**

(b) Calculate the mass of sodium hydroxide that the technician must dissolve to make her solution.

> **Maths skills** Rearrange this equation.
> concentration in g/dm^3 =
> mass of solute in volume of solution in dm^3

.... **(1 mark)**

31

Reaction yields

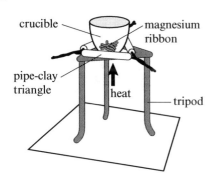

1   A student was investigating the formation of magnesium oxide by burning magnesium in air.

The balanced equation for the reaction is:

$2Mg + O_2 \rightarrow 2MgO$

The student calculated that 1.2 g of magnesium should react to produce 2.0 g of magnesium oxide.

(a) What mass of oxygen would combine with 1.2 g of magnesium to produce 2.0 g of magnesium oxide?

....

(1 mark)

> The law of conservation of mass states that no atoms are lost or made during a chemical reaction so the mass of the products equals the mass of the reactants. Use this to check your answer.

(b) If the experiment had a 50% yield, how much magnesium oxide would be obtained?

....   **(1 mark)**

(c) Why would using a loosely fitting lid on the crucible lead to a more accurate result?

....

....   **(1 mark)**

2   In the preparation of copper nitrate, copper carbonate was added a little at a time to some dilute nitric acid in a beaker until some copper carbonate was left unreacted. The equation for the reaction is:

$$CuCO_3(s) + 2HNO_3(aq) \rightarrow Cu(NO_3)_2(...) + H_2O(......) + CO_2(......)$$

(a) Complete the state symbols in the reaction above.

(3 marks)

(b) In this preparation of copper nitrate, 8.0 g of crystals were obtained. The theoretical yield is 15.0 g.

Calculate the percentage yield. Give your answer to one decimal place.

$$\% \text{ yield} = \frac{\text{mass of product actually made}}{\text{maximum theoretical mass}} \times 100$$

$$=$$

....   **(2 marks)**

(c) Suggest why the percentage yield is less than 100%.

....

....   **(2 marks)**

Atom economy

1 The atom economy of a reaction is worked out using the formula:

> You may need to use the periodic table on page 116 to calculate the relative formula mass.

$$\text{atom economy} = \frac{\text{relative formula mass of desired product from equation}}{\text{sum of relative formula masses of all reactants from equation}} \times 100$$

(a) Complete the table for the compounds in the equation:

> You will need to use the relative atomic masses in the periodic table to calculate the relative formula masses.

$$NaOH + HCl \rightarrow NaCl + H_2O$$

Reactant	Relative formula mass	Product	Relative formula mass
NaOH		NaCl	
HCl		H$_2$O	

(4 marks)

Guided

(b) Calculate the atom economy for the preparation of sodium chloride.
Give your answer to 1 decimal place.

$$\text{atom economy (\%)} = \frac{\dots\dots\dots}{(36.5 + 40) \times 100} =$$

atom economy = ...%   **(3 marks)**

2 Hydrogen can be made by reacting coal with steam. The carbon dioxide leaves the process and enters the atmosphere as a waste gas.

$$C(s) + 2H_2O(g) \rightarrow CO_2(g) + 2H_2(g)$$

(a) Calculate the atom economy of hydrogen.
Give your answer to 1 decimal place.

> Remember to use 2 × the relative formula mass of water and 2 × the relative formula mass of hydrogen.

atom economy = ...%   **(3 marks)**

(b) How could the atom economy for this process be improved?

.... **(1 mark)**

3 Alkanes can be cracked to form alkenes. Decane can be cracked to form two products as shown in the equation:

decane → ethene + octane

$$C_{10}H_{22} \rightarrow C_2H_4 + C_8H_{18}$$

(a) Calculate the atom economy for the production of ethene as the only useful product.
Give your answer to 1 decimal place.

atom economy = ...%   **(2 marks)**

(b) If both products can be sold, what is the atom economy?

.... **(1 mark)**

Reactivity series

1 In an experiment, some metals were placed into a metal salt solution and any reaction which occurred was recorded.

> A good way of tackling this question is to look at the results for each metal and note how many solutions it reacts with; the more ticks there are, the more reactive the metal.

Metal	Copper sulfate solution	Zinc sulfate solution	Iron sulfate solution
copper		✗	✗
zinc	✔		✔
iron	✔	✗	

✔ means a reaction occurred   ✗ means a reaction did not occur

(a) Use these results to put the metals in order from most reactive to least reactive.

most reactive ....

....

least reactive .... **(1 mark)**

(b) State one observation when zinc reacts with copper sulfate solution.

.... **(1 mark)**

2 Complete the following word equations.

Guided

(a) magnesium + water → magnesium hydroxide + ... **(1 mark)**

(b) calcium + nitric acid → calcium nitrate + ... **(1 mark)**

(c) zinc + hydrochloric acid → .... + ... **(1 mark)**

3 Potassium reacts with water at room temperature to produce an alkaline solution and a gas.

(a) Name the gas produced .... **(1 mark)**

(b) Name the alkaline solution .... **(1 mark)**

(c) State **two** observations for this reaction.

....

.... **(2 marks)**

4 The table below shows the results when a piece of each metal was placed in separate test tubes containing dilute hydrochloric acid.

Metal	zinc	magnesium	copper	calcium
Observations	some bubbles	bubbles and metal disappears	no reaction	vigorous bubbling, metal disappears

Which list gives the correct order of reactivity for the four metals, starting with the most reactive?

Tick **one** box.

☐ zinc, copper, magnesium, calcium   ☐ calcium, magnesium, zinc, copper

☐ magnesium, zinc, calcium, copper   ☐ copper, zinc, magnesium, calcium

(1 mark)

Oxidation, reduction and the extraction of metals

1   What is meant by the term oxidation?

Tick **one** box.

☐ gain of oxide   ☐ loss of oxygen

☐ gain of oxygen   ☐ loss of oxide   **(1 mark)**

2   Choose an element from the box to answer the following questions. Each element may be used once, more than once or not at all.

hydrogen	silver	carbon	magnesium	tin	calcium

(a) Name a metal that is found in the Earth's crust as the uncombined element.

> Think about the reactivity series to help with this question.

.... **(1 mark)**

(b) Name **two** metals that are likely to be found as compounds.

.... **(2 marks)**

(c) Name an element that can be used to reduce some metal ores.

.... **(1 mark)**

(d) Name an element that is extracted using electrolysis.

.... **(1 mark)**

3   Most metals are extracted from metal oxides found in rocks. Some metals are found as the uncombined elements.

(a) Why are some metals found as the uncombined elements?

.... **(1 mark)**

(b) In industry, iron is manufactured in the blast furnace from iron(III) oxide.

(i) Balance the equation for the reaction.

...... Fe_2O_3 + ...C → .....Fe + ...CO_2 **(1 mark)**

(ii) Write the formula of a substance which is reduced in this reaction.

.... **(1 mark)**

Guided (iii) State and explain if any substance is oxidised in this reaction.

CO has been oxidised because ....

....

....

.... **(2 marks)**

Reactions of acids

1   What type of reaction occurs when sodium hydroxide reacts with hydrochloric acid?

Tick **one** box.

☐ crystallisation   ☐ neutralisation

☐ decomposition   ☐ polymerisation

(1 mark)

2   Indigestion is caused by too much hydrochloric acid in the stomach. Some indigestion remedies contain the insoluble compounds magnesium hydroxide and aluminium hydroxide to react with the excess hydrochloric acid.

(a) What one-word term can be used to describe magnesium hydroxide and aluminium hydroxide?

....   **(1 mark)**

(b) Name the **two** salts formed when magnesium hydroxide and aluminium hydroxide react with the excess hydrochloric acid.

....   **(2 marks)**

3   Complete the table below.

> Guided

The name of the metal in the base becomes the first word in the name of the salt. The second part of the name of the salt (chloride, nitrate or sulfate), comes from the name of the acid used. The name of the first salt in the table has been completed for you.

Acid	Base	Salt
hydrochloric acid	lithium hydroxide	lithium chloride
	calcium oxide	calcium nitrate
sulfuric acid	sodium hydroxide	
	magnesium oxide	magnesium chloride

(4 marks)

4   Complete the word equations.

Remember that oxides and hydroxides are bases, and both react with acids to give a salt and water only.

(a) hydrochloric acid + ... → magnesium chloride + hydrogen   **(1 mark)**

(b) sulfuric acid + potassium hydroxide → .... + water   **(1 mark)**

(c) nitric acid + sodium carbonate → sodium nitrate + water + ...   **(1 mark)**

(d) copper oxide + sulfuric acid → water + ...   **(1 mark)**

Core practical – Salt preparation

1 In the preparation of copper sulfate crystals, a student initially added excess copper oxide to dilute sulfuric acid in a beaker with warming.

(a) What colour are copper sulfate crystals?

.... **(1 mark)**

(b) Complete the labelled diagram to show how the excess copper carbonate would be removed.   **(2 marks)**

(c) Describe how crystals of copper sulfate can be obtained from the salt solution.

....

....

.... **(2 marks)**

2 Sodium produces a salt when it reacts with dilute sulfuric acid.

> Think about the position of sodium in the reactivity series.

(a) Name the salt formed between sodium and sulfuric acid.

.... **(1 mark)**

(b) Explain why the addition of sodium metal to sulfuric acid would not be used as a method of preparing sodium sulfate in the laboratory.

....

....

....

.... **(2 marks)**

3 Describe how a sample of cobalt chloride crystals could be made from cobalt oxide and dilute hydrochloric acid.

Guided

Measure out some dilute hydrochloric acid into a beaker. Add a spatula measure

of cobalt oxide, with stirring. ....

....

....

....

....

.... **(4 marks)**

The pH scale

> Remember that the lower the pH the stronger the acid and the higher the pH the stronger the alkali.

1 The pH of some solutions is recorded in the table below.

Solution	A	B	C	D	E
pH	2	6	7	10	13

(a) Describe how a student could find the pH of an unknown solution.

....

....

....

.... **(2 marks)**

(b) Which solution in the table could be water?

.... **(1 mark)**

(c) Which solution(s) are acidic?

.... **(1 mark)**

(d) Which solution is the strongest alkali?

.... **(1 mark)**

(e) What is an aqueous solution?

.... **(1 mark)**

Guided (f) Complete the table.

Name of ion present in acid solutions	Name of ion present in alkaline solutions
	hydroxide ion

(2 marks)

2 Sulfuric acid neutralises potassium hydroxide.

(a) Write a word equation for this reaction.

.... **(1 mark)**

(b) What is neutralisation?

Tick **one** box.

☐ a reaction in which oxygen is removed

☐ a reaction in which a base and alkali cancel each other out

☐ a reaction between hydrogen ions and hydroxide ions to produce water

☐ a reaction between an acid and universal indicator **(1 mark)**

(c) What colour is universal indicator in water?

.... **(1 mark)**

Core practical – Titration

1   A student carried out a titration to find the volume of hydrochloric acid needed to neutralise 25.0 cm³ of a potassium hydroxide solution of unknown concentration. The apparatus was set up as shown.

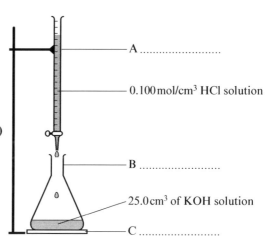

A ....

0.100 mol/cm³ HCl solution

B ....

25.0 cm³ of KOH solution

C ....

(a)   Complete the labelling of the diagram in the spaces provided.   **(3 marks)**

(b)   What piece of apparatus should be used to measure 25.0 cm³ of potassium hydroxide solution into the piece of apparatus labelled B?

.... **(1 mark)**

(c)   What is the purpose of the piece of apparatus labelled C?

.... **(1 mark)**

Guided   (d)   Methyl orange indicator is red in acid and yellow in alkali. What is the colour change in this titration?

It changes from .... to .... **(2 marks)**

Guided   (e)   Some results were recorded in the table below.

	Titration 1	Titration 2	Titration 3	Titration 4
End volume in cm³	27.25	26.85	26.10	26.40
Start volume in cm³	0.05	0.10	0.05	0.25
Titre in cm³	27.25 − 0.05 = 27.20			

   (i)   Complete the table by calculating the titre values.

   To find the titre subtract the start volume from the end volume. The first one has been done for you; now complete the rest.

   (4 marks)

   (ii)   Calculate the mean titre, using the concordant values.

   Maths skills To calculate the mean, add the results and divide by the total number of results.

   Concordant values are those within 0.10 cm³ of each other.

   ....

   .... **(2 marks)**

Extended response – Quantitative chemistry

The volumes of acid and alkali solutions that react with each other can be measured by titration using a suitable indicator. Describe how to carry out a titration to find the volume of dilute sulfuric acid needed to neutralise 25.0 cm³ of sodium hydroxide solution. You should name a suitable indicator and give the colour change that would be seen.

Remember to describe the method and to name the apparatus used to measure the different volumes.

....

....

....

....

....

....

....

....

....

....

....

....

....

....

....

....

....

....

....

....

....

....

.... **(6 marks)**

Electrolysis

1 Molten lead bromide breaks down when it conducts electricity.

(a) Using the apparatus shown, how would you know
if an electric current was passing?

.... **(1 mark)**

> **Guided**

(b) Explain why the lead bromide needs to be molten.

Solid lead bromide ....

....

....

.... **(2 marks)**

graphite
electrodes

molten
lead
bromide

(c) Name the products at each of the electrodes during this process.

....

.... **(2 marks)**

(d) Explain why graphite is used for the electrodes.

....

.... **(2 marks)**

2 When molten sodium chloride is electrolysed, reactions occur at both the cathode and the anode.

(a) Complete the table.

	Anode	Cathode
Product for electrolysis of molten sodium chloride		

(2 marks)

(b) Explain how the results are different when solid sodium chloride is used.

....

....

.... **(2 marks)**

(c) Explain what happens to metal ions during electrolysis.

> You need to mention which electrode the different ions move to, and what happens when they get there.

....

....

.... **(2 marks)**

Aluminium extraction

1   Aluminium is extracted from molten aluminium oxide by electrolysis.

(a)   Name the ions present in molten aluminium oxide and identify the electrode to which each ion moves.

> First you need to find the charge of each ion present.

name of ion:..   It moves to the ....

name of ion:..   It moves to the ....   **(2 marks)**

(b)   Write the formula of aluminium oxide.

....   **(1 mark)**

2   Aluminium is extracted from its ore using electricity. The ore, which mainly contains aluminium oxide, is mixed with cryolite before it is melted and electrolysed.

positive graphite electrode

solid crust

negative graphite electrode

molten mixture of cryolite and aluminium oxide

molten aluminium

(a)   Explain why molten aluminium oxide conducts electricity while the solid does not.

....

....   **(2 marks)**

(b)   Why is cryolite added to the aluminium oxide?

....   **(1 mark)**

> **Guided**

(c)   Why is the aluminium metal formed at the negative electrode?

Aluminium ions are positive ....

....

....   **(2 marks)**

(d)   Name **two** products that could be formed at the positive electrode during this process.

....   **(2 marks)**

(e)   What is the name of the negative electrode?

....   **(1 mark)**

(f)   Explain why the positive electrode must be continually replaced.

....

....

....

....   **(3 marks)**

Electrolysis of solutions

1 Why does calcium chloride solution conduct electricity?

Tick **one** box.

☐ It contains electrons that can move.

☐ It contains ions that can move.

☐ It contains a metal.

☐ It contains water.   **(1 mark)**

2 Name the products of electrolysis of potassium bromide solution.

Tick **one** box.

at the cathode	at the anode
☐ hydrogen	bromine
☐ hydrogen	oxygen
☐ potassium	bromine
☐ potassium	oxygen

(1 mark)

3 (a) When calcium nitrate solution is electrolysed, the product at the cathode gives a pop with a burning splint, and the product at the anode relights a glowing splint.

(i) Identify the product at the cathode.

.... **(1 mark)**

(ii) Identify the product at the anode.

.... **(1 mark)**

Guided

(b) Complete the table below to show the products at the electrodes during the electrolysis of some electrolyte solutions.

> Remember to use the reactivity series. At the cathode, hydrogen is produced if the metal is higher than hydrogen in the series. At the anode, oxygen is produced, unless the solution contains halide ions, when the halogen is produced.

Electrolyte solution	Anode	Cathode
copper chloride	chlorine	
potassium bromide	bromine	
sodium iodide		
sodium sulfate		

(4 marks)

Practical skills

Core practical – Electrolysis

1 The apparatus can be used to electrolyse some aqueous solutions.

(a) Name electrodes A and B and suggest a suitable material for the electrodes.

....

....

....**(3 marks)**

(b) Name the solute and solvent in potassium chloride solution.

solute ....

solvent .... **(2 marks)**

Guided

(c) The table below gives the observations and results of tests carried out on the products when some aqueous solutions were electrolysed.

electrolyte

electrolyte

A   B

power supply

–   +

> Remember, if a halide ion is present, then a halogen is always produced at the anode.

Complete the table. Insert answers only in the unshaded boxes.

Solution	Potassium chloride	Calcium nitrate	Sulfuric acid	Zinc bromide	Silver nitrate
Observations at cathode	colourless gas	colourless gas	colourless gas	grey solid	white solid
Observations at anode	greenish gas	colourless gas	colourless gas	orange solution	colourless gas
Test used for product at cathode	Insert a lighted splint. result – pop	Insert a lighted splint. result – pop	Insert a lighted splint. result – pop		
Test used for product at anode	Universal indicator paper turns red and bleaches.		relights a glowing splint	Universal indicator paper turns red and bleaches.	relights a glowing splint
Identity of product at cathode				zinc	silver
Identity of product at anode				bromine	

(9 marks)

(d) Explain one important safety instruction that must be followed in this practical.

....

.... **(2 marks)**

Extended response – Chemical changes

Dilute hydrochloric acid reacts with calcium hydroxide solution and with solid calcium. Compare and contrast these two reactions in terms of observations, products and equations.

> Think first of the general reactions for acids: acid + base → salt + water; acid + metal → salt + hydrogen. Then write word and balanced equations for the specific reactions.

....

....

....

....

....

....

....

....

....

....

....

....

....

....

....

....

....

....

....

....

....

....

.... **(6 marks)**

Exothermic reactions

Guided

1 In an experiment some solids were dissolved in water. The temperature of the water was initially 21°C. The figure shows the thermometer readings after dissolving the solids in water.

A
-20 -10 0 10 20 30 40 50
°C

B
-20 -10 0 10 20 30 40 50
°C

C
-20 -10 0 10 20 30 40 50
°C

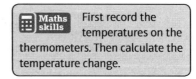

Maths skills First record the temperatures on the thermometers. Then calculate the temperature change.

Complete the table.

Solid	Initial temperature in °C	Final temperature in °C	Temperature change in °C
A	21	26	increased by 5
B	21		
C	21		

(6 marks)

Guided

2 (a) What is the law of conservation of energy?

The amount of energy in the Universe at the end of a chemical reaction is ....

.... **(2 marks)**

(b) In an exothermic reaction energy is transferred to the surroundings. Do the products have more or less energy than the reactants?

.... **(1 mark)**

3 (a) What is an exothermic reaction?

....

.... **(2 marks)**

(b) Name **two** everyday uses of exothermic reactions.

....

.... **(2 marks)**

4 Combustion reactions occur when substances react with oxygen and burn.

(a) Balance the equation for the combustion of methane CH_4.

...... CH_4 + ...O_2 →.......... CO_2 + ...H_2O

(1 mark)

(b) Describe what would happen to the temperature of the surroundings during this reaction.

.... **(1 mark)**

Endothermic reactions

1   Chemical energy changes have many uses in industry and the home. These changes, which can be exothermic or endothermic, all involve a transfer of heat energy from one place to another.

   (a)   Describe the difference between exothermic and endothermic reactions.

     An exothermic reaction ....heat energy while an endothermic reaction

     .... heat energy.   **(2 marks)**

   (b)   How could you tell if an endothermic reaction was taking place in a solution?

     ....

     .... **(2 marks)**

   (c)   Give **one** example of a chemical reaction that is endothermic.

     .... **(1 mark)**

2   The equation for the combustion of glucose is shown below.

$$C_6H_{12}O_6 + 6O_2 \rightarrow 6CO_2 + 6H_2O \text{ (+ energy)}$$

The reaction in plants that forms glucose, called photosynthesis, is shown below.

$$6CO_2 + 6H_2O \rightarrow C_6H_{12}O_6 + 6O_2$$

Use the information given above to explain if photosynthesis is an exothermic or endothermic reaction.

     ....

     ....

     .... **(2 marks)**

3   Some reactions are exothermic and some are endothermic.

   (a)   Complete the table to classify the following reactions as exothermic or as endothermic.

> Think about the temperature – if it increases, heat has been given out, or exited to the surroundings – an exothermic reaction.

Reaction	Temperature at start in °C	Temperature at end in °C	Exothermic or endothermic
A	21	50	
B	18	14	
C	20	26	
D	10	−1	

                                                                                   (4 marks)

   (b)   Calculate the temperature change for reaction A and for reaction D.

     temperature change for A = ... °C

     temperature change for D = ...°C   **(2 marks)**

Core practical – Energy changes

1 In an experiment, 25 cm³ of sodium hydroxide solution was placed, at room temperature (20 °C), in a polystyrene cup, and an excess (40 cm³) of hydrochloric acid was added. The mixture was stirred with a thermometer and the highest temperature recorded.

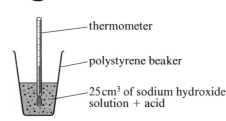
- thermometer
- polystyrene beaker
- 25 cm³ of sodium hydroxide solution + acid

> Remember that this is an acid and base reaction producing a salt and water.

(a) Write a word equation for the reaction of sodium hydroxide, with hydrochloric acid.

....

.... **(1 mark)**

(b) Why was a polystyrene cup used rather than a glass beaker?

.... **(1 mark)**

(c) Why was the solution stirred after adding the hydrochloric acid?

.... **(1 mark)**

(d) State and explain one improvement that could be made to the apparatus set up shown above.

....

.... **(2 marks)**

(e) The experiment was repeated, adding 40 cm³ of different dilute acids to 25 cm³ of sodium hydroxide solution, and the results recorded below.

	Hydrochloric acid	Ethanoic acid	Nitric acid	Sulfuric acid
Maximum temperature in °C	26.0	23.9	25.9	26.1

(i) Explain whether the reaction of sodium hydroxide with an acid is exothermic or endothermic.

....

.... **(2 marks)**

(ii) What is the independent variable in this experiment?

Tick **one** box.

☐ time taken   ☐ volume of acid

☐ type of acid   ☐ temperature   **(1 mark)**

(iii) State **one** controlled variable in this experiment.

.... **(1 mark)**

Activation energy

1 A reaction profile for a reaction is shown below.

(a) Use the words below to label each axis correctly.

- Progress of reaction   - Energy   **(1 mark)**

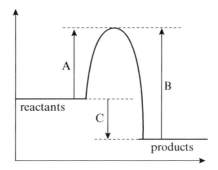

(b) Which arrow, A, B or C, represents the activation energy?

.... **(1 mark)**

(c) Which arrow, A, B or C, represents the overall energy change for this reaction?

.... **(1 mark)**

(d) Is this an exothermic reaction or an endothermic reaction?

.... **(1 mark)**

2 Classify each reaction in the energy level diagram below as exothermic or endothermic.

> Look at the position of the reactants and products.

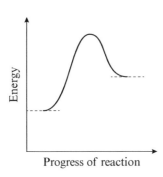

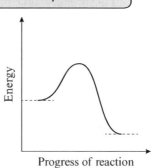

reaction 1 ....   reaction 2 ....   reaction 3 ....

(3 marks)

3 (a) What is activation energy?

> Guided

It is the energy needed ....

.... **(1 mark)**

(b) What must particles do, in order for a reaction to occur?

.... **(1 mark)**

Cells

1 Hydrogen fuel cells can be used to power cars and buses.

(a) Write a word equation for the overall reaction in a hydrogen fuel cell.

.... **(1 mark)**

(b) Draw **one** line from each type of cell to an advantage it has.

Cell

hydrogen fuel cell

rechargeable cell

Advantage

portable

not portable

The only waste product is water.

It is difficult to dispose of harmful chemicals inside it.   **(2 marks)**

(c) Describe how you would set up a simple cell in the laboratory.

....

.... **(2 marks)**

(d) Why is a battery often used instead of a cell?

.... **(1 mark)**

(e) Why can some batteries be recharged? | Think about the reaction occurring in the battery. |

.... **(1 mark)**

2 A cell was set up as shown in the diagram. Four metals, A, B, C and D, were used in turn as Metal 1, and the potential difference observed was recorded in the table below.

voltmeter

01.80

strip of copper metal

strip of Metal 1

ammonium chloride solution

Metal 1	Potential difference in V
A	+1.1
B	+2.71
C	−0.46
D	+0.58

Guided

(a) Use the results in the table to place copper and the four metals, A, B, C and D, in order of reactivity from most reactive to least reactive. Give a reason for your answer.

| If the metal is more reactive than copper then the voltage measured is positive. If the metal is less reactive than copper then the voltage measured is negative. |

B, A and D are more reactive than copper because the voltage observed is positive for B, A and D, with B more reactive than ....

.... **(3 marks)**

(b) What is the potential difference if two strips of copper are used as electrodes?

.... **(1 mark)**

(c) Name the electrolyte in this experiment.

.... **(1 mark)**

Extended response – Energy changes

Cells and fuel cells are used to generate electricity.

(a) Describe the difference between a simple cell and a fuel cell.

....

....

....

.... **(2 marks)**

(b) Describe the difference between a rechargeable cell and a non-rechargeable cell.

....

....

....

.... **(2 marks)**

(c) Evaluate the use of hydrogen fuel cells in comparison with rechargeable cells and batteries.

> When asked to evaluate, it is a good idea to give advantages and disadvantages of each.

....

....

....

....

....

....

....

....

....

....

....

....

....

....

....

.... **(4 marks)**

Rate of reaction

1 In a reaction between magnesium and hydrochloric acid the mass loss was 1.2 g in 2 minutes. Calculate the mean rate of reaction in g/s.

> Always look at the units – the rate is needed in g/s so your first step must be to convert 2 minutes to seconds.

time taken = 2 × 60 = 120 seconds

$$rate = \frac{change}{time} = \frac{1.2}{120}$$

mean rate of reaction = ... g/s   **(2 marks)**

2 A student carried out an experiment to investigate the rate of reaction between marble chips and hydrochloric acid. To follow the reaction rate the student measured the mass lost by the reaction mixture with time. The results of the experiment are shown below.

Time in min	0	1	2	3	4	5	6	7	8	9	10
Mass lost in g	0.00	0.12	0.22	0.30	0.36	0.40	0.42	0.45	0.45	0.45	0.45

(a) Calculate the mean rate of reaction in g/min between:

(i) 2 and 4 minutes $rate = \frac{change}{time} = \frac{0.36 - 0.22}{4 - 2}$

rate of reaction = ... g/min   **(2 marks)**

(ii) 4 and 6 minutes

rate of reaction = ... g/min   **(2 marks)**

(b) Draw a labelled diagram of the apparatus used to carry out this experiment.

(3 marks)

Rate of reaction on a graph

1   A student measured the loss in mass every minute during the reaction of magnesium and dilute hydrochloric acid.

> Remember that an acid and a metal produce a salt and hydrogen.

(a)   Write a word equation for the reaction of magnesium and hydrochloric acid.

    .... **(1 mark)**

(b)   The table below shows the student's results.

Time in min	0	1	2	3	4	5	6	7	8	9	10
Mass lost in g	0	0.12	0.22	0.30	0.36	0.40	0.42	0.45	0.45	0.45	0.45

- Plot the results from the table on the grid below and draw a line of best fit.

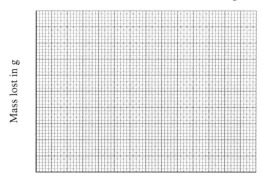

Mass lost in g

Time in min

> **Maths skills** Often there are 3 marks for drawing a graph: 1 mark for sensible scales, 1 mark for using at least half the grid and plotting all points and 1 mark for drawing a correct best fit line.

(3 marks)

2   The rate of reaction between calcium carbonate and hydrochloric acid was investigated. The graph shows the results for two different experiments.

(a)   What volume of gas is produced at 20 seconds?

experiment A ....

experiment B ....

(2 marks)

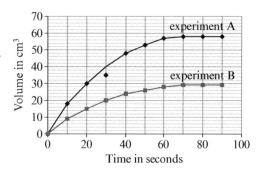

> The experiment is over when no more gas is produced and the graph is horizontal.

Guided

(b)   Calculate the difference in volume of gas produced at the end between experiment A and experiment B.

end volume for experiment A = ... end volume for experiment B = ...

difference in volume = ... **(3 marks)**

(c)   (i)   use the graph for experiment B to complete the table opposite.

Volume of gas in cm³	
Time taken in s	40

(1 mark)

(ii)   calculate the mean rate of the reaction using the results in the table and the equation:

$$\text{mean rate of reaction} = \frac{\text{volume in cm}^3}{\text{time taken in seconds}}$$

Mean rate of reaction = ...cm³/s   **(2 marks)**

Collision theory

1 When do chemical reactions occur?

Tick **one** box.

☐ when particles collide or touch

☐ when particles collide for a sufficient amount of time

☐ when particles collide with sufficient energy

☐ when particles mix together in a reaction vessel   **(1 mark)**

2 In an experiment the mass lost in a reaction between calcium carbonate and hydrochloric acid changed with time as shown in the graph.

> The rate of reaction is given by the gradient of the graph.

(a) Describe the change in the rate of reaction as time increases.

....

....

....

....   **(2 marks)**

(b) The reaction was carried out again using the same mass of calcium carbonate and the same volume of dilute hydrochloric acid at a higher temperature. Give **two** reasons why the rate of reaction increases.

Tick **two** boxes.

☐ The particles are more concentrated.

☐ The particles have a greater mass.

☐ The particles have a larger surface area.

☐ The particles have more energy.

☐ The particles move faster.   **(2 marks)**

Guided   (c) The experiment was repeated using the same mass of calcium carbonate and the same volume of hydrochloric acid, but the acid was more concentrated.

State and explain what would have happened to the rate of the reaction.

The rate of reaction would have increased. The acid was more concentrated so there were

.... particles in the .... volume so there were more ....

....

....   **(4 marks)**

Rate: pressure, surface area

1 Why does rate of reaction generally increase if the pressure is increased?

Tick **one** box.

☐ The particles move faster and there are more collisions.

☐ There are fewer particles in the same volume and there are more collisions.

☐ There are more particles in the same volume and there are more collisions.

☐ The particles have more energy and there are more collisions. **(1 mark)**

2 Which reaction will be fastest at the start of the reaction?

Tick **one** box.

☐ calcium carbonate lumps reacting with dilute nitric acid

☐ calcium carbonate lumps reacting with concentrated nitric acid

☐ calcium carbonate powder reacting with dilute nitric acid

☐ calcium carbonate powder reacting with concentrated nitric acid **(1 mark)**

3 In an experiment, a mass of magnesium ribbon reacted with excess dilute hydrochloric acid at room temperature. The volume of gas produced was recorded every 10 seconds. The results are shown in the graph as line B.

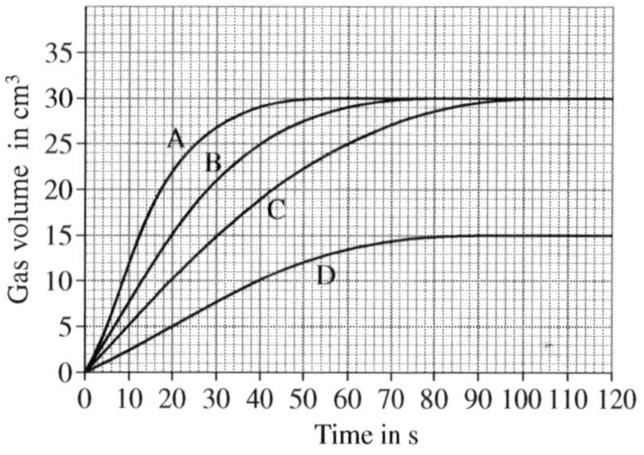

(a) At what time does the reaction for line B end?

.... **(1 mark)**

(b) Which line, A, C or D, on the graph shows the results obtained when the experiment was repeated using the same mass of magnesium powder, rather than ribbon? Give a reason for your answer.

....

.... **(2 marks)**

Guided (c) Complete the diagram to show how the experiment is carried out in the laboratory.

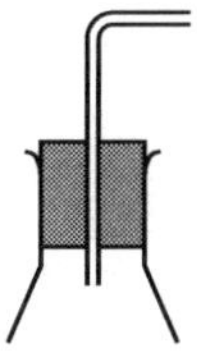

You need to complete the conical flask and then add a gas syringe to collect the gas.

What separate piece of apparatus is needed to record the volume of gas every 20 seconds?

(4 marks)

Rate: temperature

1 The time taken for a piece of magnesium to fully react with excess dilute hydrochloric acid was recorded at different temperatures. The results are shown in the table.

Temperature in °C	Time for reaction in s
20	90
30	70
40	58

Guided

(a) Use the results to determine the effect of temperature on rate of reaction.

Increasing the temperature makes the reaction .... **(1 mark)**

(b) Name the products formed in this reaction.

.... **(2 marks)**

2 A group of students was investigating the reactions between two metals and dilute hydrochloric acid. The metals used were magnesium and zinc, and they set up the experiments as shown below.

Flask A	**Flask B**	**Flask C**	**Flask D**	**Flask E**	**Flask F**
$36.5g/dm^3$ hydrochloric acid at 20°C, zinc lump	$36.5g/dm^3$ hydrochloric acid at 25°C, zinc powder	$73g/dm^3$ hydrochloric acid at 30°C, magnesium powder	$73g/dm^3$ nitric acid at 30°C, magnesium lump	$73g/dm^3$ hydrochloric acid at 20°C, magnesium lump	$73g/dm^3$ hydrochloric acid at 55°C, magnesium lump

(a) (i) In which flask would the reaction be slowest? .... **(1 mark)**

(ii) Give **two** reasons for your answer to part (i).

....

.... **(2 marks)**

(b) The students wanted to investigate how changing temperature affected the rate of reaction between metals and acid.

(i) Which **two** flasks could be used to investigate the effect of temperature?

.... **(1 mark)**

(ii) Suggest **two** other variables that would need to be kept the same to make this test fair.

> Think about the other factors that could affect the rate of reaction.

.... **(2 marks)**

3 Why does increasing temperature increase rate of reaction?

Tick **one** box.

☐ There are more frequent collisions as the particles have more energy.

☐ There are more frequent collisions as the particles move more slowly.

☐ There are more collisions per second as the particles have a greater surface area.

☐ There are more collisions per second as there are more particles present. **(1 mark)**

Practical skills

Core practical – Rate of reaction

A student used the apparatus below to investigate the effect of changing acid concentration on the rate of reaction between magnesium and dilute hydrochloric acid. Excess hydrochloric acid of different concentrations was allowed to react with 0.1 g of magnesium ribbon, and the volume of gas produced in each case was recorded every minute.

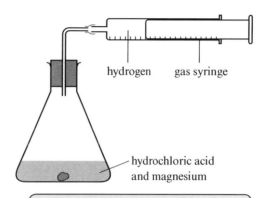

hydrogen   gas syringe

hydrochloric acid and magnesium

(a) Name one other piece of apparatus that **must** be used in this experiment.

....

(1 mark)

> Look at what the student needs to record.

(b) State **two** things that would be observed occurring in the flask during the reaction.

....

.... **(2 marks)**

> **Guided**

(c) State two ways to ensure that this experiment was a fair test.

The ....

and the ....of the

hydrochloric acid must be kept the

same in all the experiments.

(2 marks)

The results from this experiment are plotted in the graph.

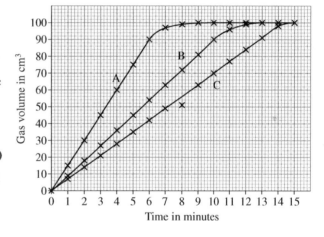

(d) Which reaction is fastest, A, B or C?

.... **(1 mark)**

(e) Which reaction, A, B or C, is carried out using the most concentrated acid?

.... **(1 mark)**

(f) Identify any anomalous results in the graph.

.... **(1 mark)**

(g) Describe another method, other than measuring the volume of gas collected, that could be used to investigate the rate of reaction between magnesium and hydrochloric acid.

> Could you use a balance?

....

....

.... **(3 marks)**

Catalysts

1 A reaction profile is shown for a catalysed reaction and an uncatalysed reaction. Label the reaction profile by adding the labels:

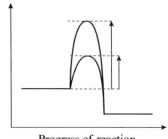

- Activation energy of catalysed reaction

- Reactants

- Products

- Energy   **(4 marks)**

Progress of reaction

2 The volume of oxygen produced when a solution of hydrogen peroxide decomposes with manganese(IV) oxide as a catalyst can be measured using the apparatus shown.

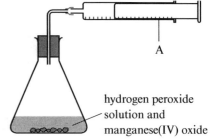

(a) What is A?

   ....

A

hydrogen peroxide solution and manganese(IV) oxide

(1 mark)

(b) The graph shows data obtained at 25°C using hydrogen peroxide solution with 1.0 g of powdered manganese(IV) oxide.

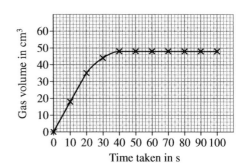

   (i) What was the total volume of gas collected?

   volume = ... cm^3

(1 mark)

Time taken in s

   (ii) The reaction was repeated using 1.0 g samples of powdered metal oxides as catalysts and hydrogen peroxide solution of the concentration at the same temperature. The time taken for the reaction was recorded for each sample in the table on the right.

Metal oxide	Time for complete decomposition in s
manganese(IV) oxide	40
copper oxide	127
zinc oxide	360

   Which one of the metal oxides was the least effective catalyst? Give a reason for your answer.

   ....

   .... **(2 marks)**

⟩ **Guided** ⟩

   (iii) The reaction was repeated with manganese(IV) oxide at 40°C and all other factors were kept the same. Sketch the graph line you would expect on the graph above.

   | This reaction is at a higher temperature so the reaction is faster. The gradient will be steeper. The first part of the line has been drawn. Now draw the rest of the line. Remember the same volume of gas will be produced but the reaction finishes faster. |

(1 mark)

Reversible reactions

1 What is a reversible reaction?

Tick **one** box.

☐ a reaction in which heat is alternately given out and taken in as the reaction proceeds

☐ a reaction in which heat is taken in

☐ a reaction in which the products of the reaction can react to produce the original reactants

☐ a reaction in which the reactants are converted into products

(1 mark)

2 In the Haber process the reaction forming ammonia from nitrogen and hydrogen can be written as shown below:

nitrogen + hydrogen ⇌ ammonia

(a) Complete the balanced equation below.

> Remember to fill in the formula first and then balance.

N_2 + ... ⇌ ....

(2 marks)

(b) How does the equation show that this reaction is reversible?

....

....

(1 mark)

> **Guided**

3 Methane can be formed when carbon monoxide reacts with hydrogen:

$CO(g) + 3H_2(g) \rightleftharpoons CH_4(g) + H_2O(g)$

(a) What does the double arrow (⇌) between reactants and products mean?

This means the reaction goes ....

(1 mark)

(b) Name the molecules that will be present when this reaction has been left for some time.

....

....

(2 marks)

4 The reaction between anhydrous copper sulfate and water to give hydrated copper sulfate is a reversible reaction. It is exothermic in one direction and endothermic in the opposite direction.

anhydrous copper sulfate + water ⇌ hydrated copper sulfate

(a) Which direction of the reaction is the endothermic direction?

.... **(1 mark)**

(b) What is the colour change when water is added to anhydrous copper sulfate?

.... **(2 marks)**

(c) What does hydrated mean?

.... **(1 mark)**

Equilibrium

1 Hydrogen can be made by reacting methane with steam as shown in the equation below:

methane + steam → hydrogen + carbon monoxide

$CH_4(g) + H_2O(g) \rightarrow 3H_2(g) + CO(g)$

This reaction is reversible and an equilibrium can be reached.

(a) What does **equilibrium** mean?

....

.... **(2 marks)**

(b) State a necessary condition for equilibrium to occur in a reversible reaction.

.... **(1 mark)**

2 The graph shows how the yield of
ammonia, in the Haber process, is affected
by changes to temperature and pressure.

(a) State the effect of increasing the
pressure on the yield of ammonia
at 400 °C.

....

....

....

....

(1 mark)

[Graph: y-axis "% ammonia" from 0 to 100; x-axis "Pressure in atmospheres" from 0 to 1000. Curves labelled 200 °C, 300 °C, 400 °C, 500 °C, 600 °C, 700 °C.]

> Look at the yield for the same pressure but
> different temperatures.

(b) State the effect of changing the temperature on the yield of ammonia.

....

.... **(1 mark)**

(c) What is the % yield of ammonia when the temperature is 400 °C and the pressure is 200 atm?

.... **(1 mark)**

(d) What type of reaction *must* the Haber process be if equilibrium is to occur?

Tick **one** box.

☐ exothermic

☐ endothermic

☐ neutralisation

☐ reversible   **(1 mark)**

Practical skills

Extended response – Rates of reaction

Magnesium reacts with dilute hydrochloric acid. A student has been asked to investigate how the rate of this reaction changes when the concentration of hydrochloric acid is changed.
Write a plan the student could use.

> Write a word equation for the reaction, and study it to help you decide what to measure. Make sure your plan includes how you will ensure the experiment is a fair test.

....

....

....

....

....

....

....

....

....

....

....

....

....

....

....

....

....

....

....

....

....

....

.... **(6 marks)**

> For a fair test, make sure you have controlled all the factors that might affect the rate.

Crude oil

1 Which word below best describes crude oil?

Tick **one** box.

☐ compound

☐ electrolyte

☐ mixture

☐ polymer

(1 mark)

2 The first process in oil refining separates the crude oil into fractions.

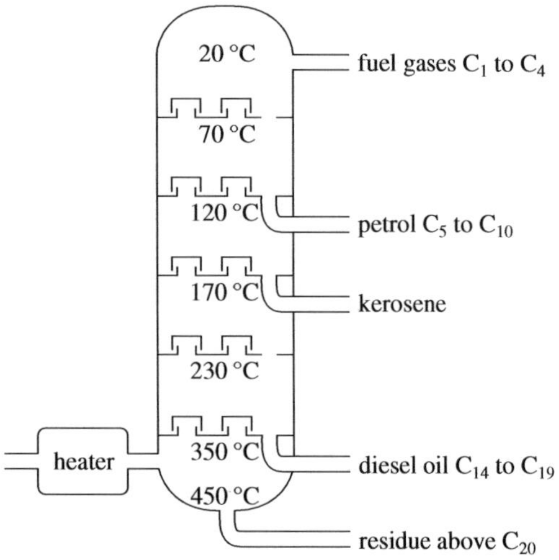

(a) Suggest a range of molecular sizes for kerosene.

....

(1 mark)

(b) (i) Which fraction has the highest boiling point?

....

(1 mark)

20 °C ── fuel gases C_1 to C_4

70 °C

120 °C ── petrol C_5 to C_{10}

170 °C ── kerosene

230 °C

heater ── 350 °C ── diesel oil C_{14} to C_{19}

450 °C

── residue above C_{20}

(ii) Which fraction will contain the molecules shown below?

Count the carbon atoms in the structures.

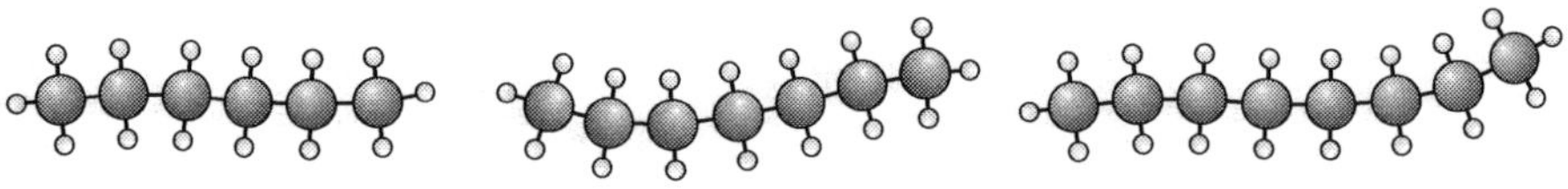

.... **(1 mark)**

(c) What is the name for the method of separation shown in the diagram?

.... **(1 mark)**

(d) How does the number of carbon atoms in each fraction affect the boiling point range of the fraction?

.... **(1 mark)**

(e) The fractions can be processed to produce fuels and feedstock for the petrochemical industry.

(i) Name **two** fractions that can be processed to produce fuel.

1. .... 2. .... **(2 marks)**

Guided

(ii) Name **three** useful materials beside fuel on which modern life depends that are produced by the petrochemical industry.

1. solvents   2. ....   3. .... **(3 marks)**

Alkanes

1 Crude oil is a mixture of different hydrocarbons.

(a) What is a hydrocarbon?

....

.... **(2 marks)**

(b) The table gives information about hydrocarbons called alkanes.

Alkanes	Formula	Boiling point in °C
	CH_4	−162
ethane	C_2H_6	−89
propane		
butane	C_4H_{10}	0
pentane	C_5H_{12}	+36

(i) Give the name for the alkane with the formula CH_4 .... **(1 mark)**

(ii) Estimate the boiling point of propane °C .... **(1 mark)**

(iii) Give the formula for the alkane called propane .... **(1 mark)**

2 Draw the structure of:

Guided

(a) butane

Butane has four carbon atoms in each molecule. These have been drawn for you. Now complete the structure by making sure each carbon atom has four bonds, with hydrogen atoms attached.

$$C — C — C — C$$

(1 mark)

(b) ethane

(1 mark)

(c) an alkane with five carbon atoms in its molecule

(1 mark)

3 Which hydrocarbon is not an alkane?

Tick **one** box.

☐ CH_4 ☐ C_3H_8 ☐ C_4H_8 ☐ C_5H_{12}

Use the general formula for alkanes to help.   **(1 mark)**

Properties of hydrocarbons

1 (a) Balance the equation for the hydrocarbon burning:

.... C_3H_8 + ... $O_2 \rightarrow$ .... CO_2 + ... H_2O **(1 mark)**

(b) Name the hydrocarbon C_3H_8.

.... **(1 mark)**

Guided

2 The diagram shows the apparatus used to investigate the products of combustion of hydrocarbons.

(a) Describe what the student would observe happening in tube A and tube B when the hydrocarbon had been burning for a few minutes.

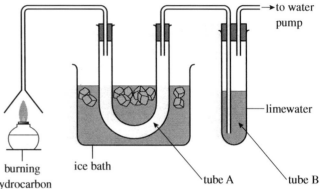

In tube A, a colourless .... is formed.

In tube B, the limewater changes from ....

to ....

(3 marks)

> 🧪 **Practical skills** When describing observations, describe what you **see** happening rather than giving the names of products.

(b) Name a substance which could be used to show that water is present in tube A and state the observations.

....

....

.... **(3 marks)**

(c) Complete the equation below:

hydrocarbon + oxygen $\rightarrow$ .... **(2 marks)**

3 Pentane (C_5H_{12}) and octane (C_8H_{18}) are both alkanes.

(a) Which of these alkanes has the higher boiling point? Give a reason for your answer.

....

.... **(2 marks)**

(b) Which of these alkanes is more flammable?

.... **(1 mark)**

(c) Petrol is liquid fuel used to power motor car engines. Give two properties of petrol that makes it suitable to be used in this way.

....

.... **(2 marks)**

Cracking

1   What type of reaction is cracking?

Tick **one** box.

☐ displacement

☐ exothermic

☐ neutralisation

☐ thermal decomposition

(1 mark)

2   Hydrocarbons can be cracked.

(a)   What does 'cracking' mean?

....

.... **(2 marks)**

(b)   Complete the equation for the cracking of octane, C_8H_{18}.

$C_8H_{18} \rightarrow C_6H_{14} +$ ....   **(1 mark)**

> Guided

(c)   Name **two** methods of cracking.

1. catalytic

2. ....   **(2 marks)**

(d)   Suggest two reasons why there is greater demand for the products of cracking than for C_8H_{18}.

....

.... **(2 marks)**

3   Fractional distillation separates crude oil into fractions of similar hydrocarbons. The table below compares the fractions obtained from crude oil from three different sources.

Fraction	Crude oil A content in %	Crude oil B content in %	Crude oil C content in %
fuel gases	6	4	9
petrol and naphtha	10	6	19
diesel and kerosene	15	10	18
fuel oil	17	20	21
bitumen and residue	52	60	33

> Check back to page 62 if you have forgotten the sizes of molecules present in the different fractions.

(a)   Which fraction has the largest molecules?

.... **(1 mark)**

(b)   Which crude oil, A, B or C, has the highest viscosity?

.... **(1 mark)**

Alkenes

1   Which of the following shows the structure of an alkene molecule?

Tick **one** box.

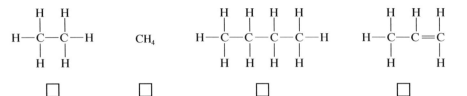

☐   ☐   ☐   ☐   **(1 mark)**

2   The diagram shows some examples of hydrocarbons that could be found in products from crude oil.

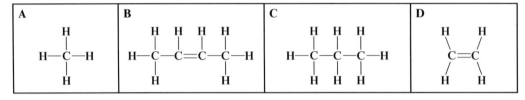

(a)   The two hydrocarbons that are unsaturated are .... and ....   **(1 mark)**

(b)   The chemical name for compound A is methane. State the chemical names for compounds
C and D.

....   **(2 marks)**

(c)   Why are substances A, B, C and D all described as hydrocarbons?

....

....   **(2 marks)**

(d)   Complete and balance the equation for the complete
combustion of substance A, CH_4.

$CH_4 + ...O_2 \rightarrow$ ....
                                                    (2 marks)

> All hydrocarbons burn to form
> carbon dioxide and water.
> Write the formulae of these
> products, and then balance
> the equation.

(e)   What is the general formula of an alkene?

....   **(1 mark)**

3   A hydrocarbon, **Z**, has the formula C_xH_y. The hydrocarbon undergoes complete combustion as shown
in the equation:

$$C_xH_y + 6O_2 \rightarrow 4CO_2 + 4H_2O$$

(a)   Determine the values of x and y using the equation given above.

....   **(2 marks)**

(b)   Name hydrocarbon **Z**. ....   **(1 mark)**

(c)   Draw a displayed structure of a molecule of hydrocarbon **Z**.

(1 mark)

Reactions of alkenes

1   Which of the following undergoes an addition reaction with bromine?

Tick **one** box.

☐ dibromoethane   ☐ ethene

☐ ethane   ☐ propane   **(1 mark)**

2   Below are three organic compounds, A, B and C.

A   **B**   **C**

(a) What is the functional group in compound A?

> A functional group in a molecule is the group of atoms that gives it its distinctive properties.

.... **(1 mark)**

(b) Name the products formed when compound A undergoes complete combustion.

.... **(2 marks)**

(c) Name the products, which are compounds, that are formed when compound A undergoes incomplete combustion.

.... **(2 marks)**

(d) Which substance can react with compound A to form compound C?

Tick **one** box.

☐ chlorine   ☐ hydrogen

☐ bromine   ☐ water   **(1 mark)**

(e) Name compound C.

.... **(1 mark)**

(f) Which of the compounds, A, B and C, are hydrocarbons?

.... **(1 mark)**

(g) Which of the compounds, A, B and C, are saturated?

> Look for substances which have no C=C bonds.

.... **(1 mark)**

3   (a) Name a substance which can be used to distinguish between an alkane and an alkene.

.... **(1 mark)**

(b) What is observed when this substance is added to an alkane and to an alkene?

alkane ....

alkene .... **(2 marks)**

Alcohols

1   A molecule of ethanol has 8 single covalent bonds. Draw the missing bonds on the figure to complete the displayed formula for ethanol.

H   H

H   C   C   O   H

H   H

(1 mark)

2   The fourth member of the alcohol series is called butanol. Its structure is shown.

H   H   H   H
| | | |
H—C—C—C—C—O—H
| | | |
H   H   H   H

(a) What is the functional group in the butanol molecule? ....

.... **(1 mark)**

(b) What is the molecular formula of butanol? ....

.... **(1 mark)**

3   (a) What **two** products would be formed by the complete combustion of butanol?

.... **(2 marks)**

 (b) Suggest **two** possible uses for butanol.

Butanol could be used as a solvent or as a .... **(2 marks)**

4   Which of the following shows the structure of a molecule of propanol?

Tick **one** box.

H   H
| |
H—C—C—OH
| |
H   H
☐

H   H   O
| | //
H—C—C—C
| | \
H   H   O—H
☐

H   H   H
| | |
H—C—C—C—O—H
| | |
H   H   H
☐

H   H   H
| | |
H—C=C—C—H
| |
H   H
☐

(1 mark)

5   Ethanol is produced by fermentation of sugars.

Describe the conditions needed for fermentation.

....

....

....

....

.... **(3 marks)**

Carboxylic acids

 1 Complete the displayed formula for ethanoic acid. You may use single and double covalent bonds.

 You need to use one double bond.

H

H   C   C   O

H   O   H

(1 mark)

 2 The structural formula of one carboxylic acid is:

(a) Draw a circle around the functional group of the carboxylic acid shown above.   **(1 mark)**

(b) Name the carboxylic acid shown above.

....   **(1 mark)**

(c) Write the molecular formula for this carboxylic acid.

....   **(1 mark)**

(d) Will this acid dissolve in water?

....   **(1 mark)**

3 (a) Name the alcohol that could be oxidised to make butanoic acid.

....   **(1 mark)**

(b) What gas is produced when carboxylic acids, like propanoic acid and butanoic acid, react with metal carbonates?

....   **(1 mark)**

Guided   (c) Describe another common reaction of carboxylic acids, naming the general reactant and product involved.

Carboxylic acids react with alcohols, forming ....

....   **(2 marks)**

Polymers

1   Which molecule can be used to make an addition polymer?

Tick **one** box.

☐   ethane

☐   chloroethene

☐   fluoroethane

☐   poly(propene)   **(1 mark)**

2   Most polymers are made from molecules obtained by the refining of crude oil.

     (a)   The diagram below shows the formation of one particular polymer. Write the names of the reactants and product in this reaction.

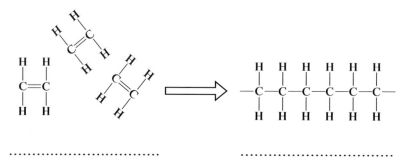

      ....

                                                          (2 marks)

> **Guided**   (b)   Describe what polymers are and how they are formed.

      Polymers are long ....

      made by .... many ....

      ....   **(2 marks)**

3   The equation below shows the formation of a polymer from its monomer.

$$n \; \underset{\underset{H}{|}}{\overset{\overset{H}{|}}{C}} = \underset{\underset{H}{|}}{\overset{\overset{H}{|}}{C}} \longrightarrow \left[\underset{\underset{H}{|}}{\overset{\overset{H}{|}}{C}} - \underset{\underset{H}{|}}{\overset{\overset{H}{|}}{C}} \right]_{n}$$

     (a)   Name the monomer.

      ....   **(1 mark)**

     (b)   Name the polymer.

      ....   **(1 mark)**

     (c)   What type of reaction is this?

      ....   **(2 marks)**

DNA

1   Tick the name of **two** naturally occurring polymers which are essential for the life of human organisms.

Tick **two** boxes.

☐ poly(ethene)   ☐ poly(propene)

☐ protein   ☐ starch

☐ polyester   **(2 marks)**

2   The diagram shows part of a DNA molecule.

> A
> T
> C
> G

(a)   What does the abbreviation DNA stand for?

.... **(1 mark)**

(b)   State one function of DNA.

....

.... **(1 mark)**

(c)   Name the shape of DNA.

.... **(1 mark)**

(d)   How many

     (i)   polymer chains are present in DNA?

.... **(1 mark)**

     (ii)   different monomers are present in this molecule?

> Remember that a monomer is the repeating unit.

.... **(1 mark)**

3   Cellulose is an important polymer found in plants.

(a)   Name the monomer from which cellulose is made.

.... **(1 mark)**

(b)   Name one other naturally occurring polymer which contains the same monomer.

.... **(1 mark)**

Extended response – Organic chemistry

A dilute solution of ethanol can be produced in the laboratory by fermentation. It can then be concentrated by distillation, as shown in the diagram below. Describe the processes of fermentation and of distillation.

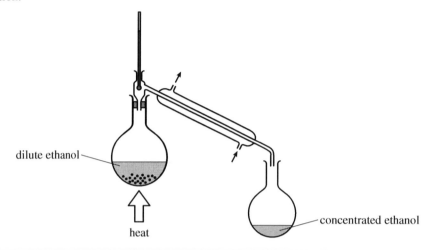

dilute ethanol

heat

concentrated ethanol

> When describing fermentation you need to state the starting materials. The question also asks about distillation, so you should describe how the apparatus can be used to concentrate the ethanol.

....

....

....

....

....

....

....

....

....

....

....

....

....

....

.... **(6 marks)**

Practical skills

Pure substances and formulations

1 Describe the difference between a pure substance in chemistry and a pure substance in everyday life.

....

....

.... **(2 marks)**

2 A solid is thought to be pure aspirin. Which is the best way to test its purity?

Tick **one** box.

☐ Determine its density.   ☐ Determine its melting point.

☐ Determine the pH.   ☐ Determine its flame colour.

(1 mark)

3 Which substance is a formulation?

Tick **one** box.

☐ air   ☐ steel

☐ iron   ☐ gold

(1 mark)

4 The table shows some data about elements and formulations.

Substance	Melting point in °C	Boiling point in °C
A	420	913
B	1420–1536	2535–2545
C	−33	355

(a) Classify the substances in the table as solids, liquids or gases at room temperature (20 °C).

> If the melting point is above 20 °C, then the substance is a solid at room temperature.

....

.... **(3 marks)**

(b) Classify the substances in the table as elements or formulations. Give reasons for your answers.

....

....

.... **(3 marks)**

5 The melting point of a substance was determined. How can this melting point be used to identify the substance?

.... **(1 mark)**

Core practical – Chromatography

1 A student used the apparatus shown to separate the substances mixed together in some purple food dye.

(a) Describe each part of the apparatus set-up.

A ....

B ....

C beaker

D ....   **(4 marks)**

(b) Describe what is wrong with the set-up and give a reason why it will not work as shown.

....

....   **(2 marks)**

2 A student investigated an orange drink in the laboratory using chromatography, to determine whether the drink contained dyes X, Y and Z. The results are shown, right.

(a) How many dyes were in the orange drink?

....

(1 mark)

(b) Why is the start line drawn in pencil?

....   **(1 mark)**

(c) Explain if dye Z is a pure substance.

....

....   **(1 mark)**

(d) Use the figure to complete the table.

	Distance in cm
Distance moved by dye X	
Distance moved from start line by solvent	

Use the equation:

$$R_f = \frac{\text{distance moved by dye X}}{\text{distance moved by solvent}}$$

Calculate the R_f value for dye X.

> You need to use a ruler to help you.

$R_f X = $ ....   **(4 marks)**

Tests for gases

1   Which of the following is used to test for the presence of chlorine?

Tick **one** box.

☐ Put a glowing splint into a test tube of the gas.

☐ Put a burning splint into a test tube of the gas.

☐ Bubble the gas through limewater.

☐ Put a piece of damp litmus paper into the gas.   **(1 mark)**

2   A burning splint is lowered into a gas jar. Which gas, if present in the jar, will allow the splint to burn vigorously?

Tick **one** box.

☐ carbon dioxide

☐ helium

☐ neon

☐ oxygen   **(1 mark)**

3   Calcium carbonate and dilute hydrochloric acid were reacted in a test tube and the gas produced was bubbled into limewater.

calcium carbonate + hydrochloric acid

test tube A   test tube B

(a) Write a word equation for the reaction of calcium carbonate with hydrochloric acid.

> What gas is produced when an acid and carbonate react?

.... **(1 mark)**

(b) State what was observed in test tube B.

....

.... **(2 marks)**

Guided   (c) Write the chemical name and formula for limewater.

name *calcium hydroxide solution*

formula .... **(2 marks)**

Tests for cations

1 A student tested a metal chloride solution with sodium hydroxide solution.

A blue precipitate formed. What was the metal ion in the metal chloride solution?

Tick **one** box.

☐ calcium ion   ☐ iron(II) ion

☐ copper(II) ion   ☐ iron(III) ion   **(1 mark)**

2 Which solution will give a coloured precipitate when a few drops of sodium hydroxide solution are added?

Tick **one** box.

☐ aluminium sulfate solution   ☐ iron(II) sulfate solution

☐ calcium nitrate solution   ☐ magnesium nitrate solution   **(1 mark)**

3 A forensic scientist working at a crime scene tested an unknown solid found on a suspect's shoe. The results of her observations are shown below.

Appearance	Solubility	Test 1: Flame test	Test 2: Effect of adding dilute hydrochloric acid
white solid	insoluble	red flame	bubbles of gas formed that turns limewater cloudy

> **Practical skills** You need to learn the flame colours produced by the following ions: lithium, sodium, potassium, calcium and copper.

(a) Describe how to carry out a flame test.

....

....

....   **(3 marks)**

> **Guided**

(b) Why are at least two tests needed to identify any ionic substance?

Ionic substances contain two ions and ....   **(2 marks)**

(c) Name the gas that is tested for in test 2. ....   **(1 mark)**

(d) Suggest a possible name for the unknown white solid. ....   **(1 mark)**

> **Guided**

4 The effect of adding sodium hydroxide solution to solutions of different metal ions is shown in the table below.

Cation	Symbol	Effect of adding sodium hydroxide solution
aluminium	$Al^{3+}(aq)$	white solid formed
magnesium	$Mg^{2+}(aq)$	white solid formed
copper(II)		blue solid formed
iron(II)	$Fe^{2+}(aq)$	solid formed
iron(III)	$Fe^{3+}(aq)$	solid formed

(a) Name the type of reaction that occurs in these tests. ....   **(1 mark)**

(b) Complete the missing information in the table. ....   **(3 marks)**

Tests for anions

1 Which solution forms a white precipitate when silver nitrate solution is added?

Tick **one** box.

☐ potassium bromide   ☐ potassium chloride

☐ potassium iodide   ☐ sodium sulfate   **(1 mark)**

Guided 2 A group of students were given a white soluble solid that was thought to be either potassium carbonate or potassium sulfate.

Describe how they could test the white solid to see if it contained carbonate ions or sulfate ions.

First add hydrochloric acid. If carbonate ions are present a gas is produced that will turn

....

To test for sulfate ions add ....

.... **(2 marks)**

3 Describe how to carry out **one** test for each pair of substances to identify which is which. Use chemicals from the list in the box.

barium chloride solid	distilled water	hydrochloric acid solution
nitric acid solution	silver nitrate solid	sodium hydroxide solution

(a) Sodium bromide and sodium chloride.

....

....

....

....

....

.... **(3 marks)**

> Remember that barium chloride and silver nitrate are usually used in solution in anion tests.

(b) Sodium sulfate and sodium chloride.

....

....

....

....

....

....

....

.... **(5 marks)**

Flame emission spectroscopy

1 Which method is best for analysing a solution in order to determine if it contains both magnesium ions and calcium ions?

Tick **one** box.

☐ adding a few drops of sodium hydroxide solution

☐ adding a few drops of nitric acid solution

☐ carrying out flame emission spectroscopy

☐ carrying out a flame test

> Do both ions have a characteristic flame test colour?

(1 mark)

2 The flame emission spectra of four metal ions and of one mixture of two metal ions are shown below.

Li^+

Na^+

Ca^{2+}

Cu^{2+}

Mixture

(a) Use the spectra to identify the two metal ions in the mixture.

.... **(2 marks)**

(b) Describe how a sample is analysed in a flame emission spectrometer.

....

....

.... **(3 marks)**

(c) Give two advantages of using flame emission spectroscopy, rather than chemical tests, to identify the ions in a mixture.

....

.... **(2 marks)**

(d) Write the electronic structure of a potassium ion.

> The potassium atom has 19 electrons. First write the electronic structure of the atom. Then, remember that the potassium ion is K^+, so it has lost one electron.

.... **(1 mark)**

Core practical – Identifying a compound

1   Solid A is thought to be an aluminium or magnesium halide. In an experiment to identify the metal ion in A, a student first made a solution of A.

(a) Describe how a solution of A was made.

....

....

.... **(2 marks)**

(b) What solution is added to the solution of A to identify the metal ion?

.... **(1 mark)**

(c) To identify the halide ion a few drops of nitric acid solution were added followed by a few drops of solution X. Name solution X.

.... **(1 mark)**

2   A **mixture** of two ionic compounds was analysed to determine the ions present in the mixture. The two ionic compounds have the **same anion**.

The results of the tests are given in the table below.

Description of test	Observations
test 1 flame test	yellow flame
test 2 A sample of the mixture was dissolved in deionised water and sodium hydroxide solution was added.	white precipitate, which dissolves in excess sodium hydroxide solution
test 3 A sample of the mixture was dissolved in deionised water, and nitric acid and drops of silver nitrate solution were added.	no effervescence, yellow precipitate

Use the information in the table to answer the questions below.

(a) Using the evidence from test 1, name one cation present in the mixture.

.... **(1 mark)**

(b) Using the evidence from test 2, name the other cation present.

.... **(1 mark)**

(c) Using the evidence from test 3, write the formula of the anion present in the mixture.

.... **(1 mark)**

(d) Suggest the name of **one** compound present in the mixture.

> You could use either of the cations with the anion.

.... **(1 mark)**

Extended response – Chemical analysis

Plan an experiment to positively identify each ion in unlabelled samples of each of the following solutions:

- magnesium sulfate solution
- sodium chloride solution
- iron(II) iodide solution
- magnesium bromide solution.

> What cation tests do you need to use?
> What anion tests do you need to use?

....

....

....

....

....

....

....

....

....

....

....

....

....

....

....

....

....

....

....

....

....

....

.... **(6 marks)**

The early atmosphere and today's atmosphere

1   Which unreactive gas makes up most of the Earth's atmosphere today?

Tick **one** box.

☐ carbon dioxide

☐ helium

☐ nitrogen

☐ oxygen   **(1 mark)**

2   The proportions of the main gases in our atmosphere have not changed much over the past 200 million years.

(a) Complete the table to show the percentages of the **two** main gases in the Earth's atmosphere.

Main gas	% in atmosphere
	20

(2 marks)

(b) The atmosphere also contains small amounts of other gases, for example argon, water vapour, carbon dioxide and hydrogen.

Which of these other gases is a noble gas? ....   **(1 mark)**

(c) Name **two** gases that were present in the early atmosphere, which are not present in today's atmosphere.

....

....   **(2 marks)**

3   A group of students burned some magnesium in air. The volume of air reduced as the magnesium reacted with the oxygen in the air. The students recorded the volumes of air.

The results of their experiment are shown below.

Starting volume in cm³	Temperature in °C	Final volume in cm³	Temperature in °C
200	20	172	20

(a) Complete the balanced symbol equation for the reaction of magnesium with oxygen.

.... Mg + ... → .... MgO   **(2 marks)**

(b) What is the volume of oxygen in the sample?

Write down the volume of oxygen at the start, and subtract the volume of oxygen at the end.

....   **(1 mark)**

(c) Calculate the percentage of oxygen in the sample.

.... **(2 marks)**

Evolution of the atmosphere

Guided

1 The table below shows the main gases in the Earth's atmosphere today and 3.5 billion years ago.

Earth's atmosphere today	Early Earth's atmosphere (3500 million years ago)
nitrogen 78%	carbon dioxide 95.5%
oxygen 20%	nitrogen 3.1%
argon 0.9%	argon 1.2%
carbon dioxide 0.04%	methane 0.2%

(a) Compare the composition of gases in the Earth's early atmosphere with the atmosphere today.

The early atmosphere contained no oxygen, but ....

....

....

.... **(3 marks)**

(b) Explain why the data on the Earth's atmosphere today will be more accurate than the data on the early Earth's atmosphere.

....

.... **(1 mark)**

(c) Scientists think that the atmosphere has changed due to the presence of plants and algae on the Earth. Explain how the presence of algae and plants could change the atmosphere.

> Think about the chemical reactions in plants that use gases from the air for life processes.

....

....

.... **(2 marks)**

2 When carbon dioxide dissolves in water carbonic acid is formed.

(a) Complete the balanced symbol equation for this chemical reaction, including state symbols.

$H_2O(l) +$ .... $\rightarrow H_2CO_3(aq)$ **(1 mark)**

(b) Some sea creatures need the carbon dioxide for growth.

  (i) What do some marine animals make with the dissolved carbon dioxide?

  .... **(1 mark)**

  (ii) What kind of sedimentary rocks do they eventually form?

  .... **(1 mark)**

(c) Algae and plants produced the oxygen that is now in the atmosphere by photosynthesis. Balance the equation for this reaction.

....CO_2 + ...$H_2O \rightarrow$ ....$C_6H_{12}O_6$ + ...O_2 **(1 mark)**

Greenhouse gases

1 Which is **not** a greenhouse gas?

Tick **one** box.

☐ carbon dioxide   ☐ oxygen

☐ methane   ☐ water vapour   **(1 mark)**

2 The graph shows how the percentage of carbon dioxide in the atmosphere has changed over the past 4500 million years.

(a) What was the percentage of carbon dioxide in the atmosphere 4000 million years ago?

.... **(1 mark)**

Guided (b) Carbon dioxide is a greenhouse gas. Name, and give the formula of, **two** other greenhouse gases.

water vapour, which has formula ...., and ....

.... **(4 marks)**

(c) State **two** conclusions that can be drawn from the graph.

> Look at what is happening to the % of carbon dioxide – does it increase or decrease?

....

....

....

.... **(2 marks)**

(d) It is thought that the percentage of carbon dioxide in the atmosphere has changed in the last 100 years.

State **two** human activities that may have contributed to this change.

....

.... **(2 marks)**

Global climate change

Guided

1 Due to human activity the levels of carbon dioxide in our atmosphere have been increasing over the last 100 years.

(a) Explain why destroying large areas of forest causes increased levels of carbon dioxide in the atmosphere.

During photosynthesis plants take in ....

.... **(2 marks)**

(b) Describe how one other human activity is thought to be responsible for increasing carbon dioxide levels in the atmosphere.

....

.... **(2 marks)**

(c) Describe **two** environmental problems caused by the increased levels of carbon dioxide.

....

.... **(2 marks)**

2 The graph shows the changes in average world temperatures and carbon dioxide levels over the past few thousand years.

(a) Describe the relationship between carbon dioxide levels and average world temperatures shown by the graph.

> From the graph decide what happens to temperature if the carbon dioxide level increases.

Vostok (Antarctica) ice core records

Temperature change in °C

4
2
0
22
24
26
28
210

CO$_2$ concentration in ppm

400
360
320
280
240
200

400 350 300 250 200 150 100 50 0
Years before present in thousands

....

....

.... **(2 marks)**

(b) An increase in global temperature may cause climate change. What is one possible effect of climate change?

Tick **one** box.

☐ acid rain   ☐ ice caps melting

☐ global dimming   ☐ volcanic activity   **(1 mark)**

(c) Define global warming.

....

.... **(1 mark)**

Carbon footprint

1 What is meant by the term carbon footprint?

Tick **one** box.

☐ the amount of carbon in a substance

☐ the total amount of carbon dioxide emitted over the full life cycle of a substance

☐ the total amount of all greenhouse gases emitted over the full life cycle of a substance

☐ the percentage of carbon dioxide formed from burning a substance   **(1 mark)**

2 The graph shows some factors that contribute to the carbon footprint of an average person living in the UK.

(a) What percentage of the footprint comes from water heating?

.... **(1 mark)**

(b) What percentage of the footprint comes from travel?

Remember to include all types of travel.

.... **(1 mark)**

(c) State **two** ways in which the percentage in (b) could be reduced.

....

.... **(2 marks)**

Guided (d) To reduce the carbon footprint due to electricity generation from fossil fuels, alternative energy sources can be used, or carbon capture and storage could be introduced.

State **two** alternative energy sources.

solar power and ....

.... **(2 marks)**

(e) A carbon footprint can be reduced by reducing emissions of two different gases. Name these **two** gases.

.... **(2 marks)**

Atmospheric pollution

1 The gas emitted from a power station chimney contained the gases shown in the table.

> Guided

Gas	Abundance as a %
nitrogen	66
carbon dioxide	18
oxygen	10
sulfur dioxide	

(a) Calculate the percentage of sulfur dioxide present in the chimney gas.

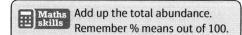

Maths skills   Add up the total abundance. Remember % means out of 100.

(2 marks)

(b) Name **one** pollutant gas from the table.

.... **(1 mark)**

2 Burning fuels that contain carbon can produce carbon dioxide, carbon monoxide and soot (carbon).

(a) Which of these products are **not** formed by complete combustion of the fuel?

.... **(1 mark)**

(b) All three of the products can cause different environmental problems.

Describe **one** problem caused by each of the three products.

....

....

.... **(3 marks)**

3 When petrol burns in an engine, several pollutants are formed.

(a) Complete the table.

Name of pollutant	Formula	Effect of pollutant
sulfur dioxide		acid rain/respiratory problems
	CO	toxic – can cause suffocation
	C	
nitrogen oxides	NOx	

(5 marks)

(b) How does sulfur dioxide form when petrol burns?

.... **(1 mark)**

(c) How does CO form when petrol burns?

.... **(1 mark)**

Extended response –
The atmosphere

The graph shows how the concentration of carbon dioxide in the atmosphere has changed from the year 1000 to the year 2000.

Describe and account for the change in concentration of carbon dioxide in the atmosphere and why it is an area of concern.

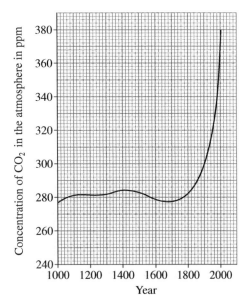

> What human activities increase the amount of carbon dioxide in the atmosphere?

....

....

....

....

....

....

....

....

....

....

....

....

....

.... **(6 marks)**

The Earth's resources

1 Energy resources that, once used, can replenish themselves and so more can be used are called:

Tick **one** box.

☐ finite

☐ kinetic

☐ non-renewable

☐ renewable **(1 mark)**

2 Which of the energy sources listed is not a renewable source of energy?

Tick **one** box.

☐ oil

☐ solar

☐ tidal

☐ wind **(1 mark)**

3 We use energy for transport, power generation and in our factories and homes. Some energy sources are shown in the table below. Complete the table.

> Renewable means it can be replaced in a human lifetime.

	Energy source	Finite or renewable
biodiesel	processing of plant oils	
coal	deep mining or opencast mining	
ethanol	fermentation of sugars from plants	
wind power	wind driving turbines	
petrol	fractional distillation of crude oil	

(5 marks)

Guided

4 Products can be classified as natural or as synthetic. Draw one line from each product to the correct classification.

Product   **Classification**

wool ─────────────────────────┐

plastic   natural

cotton

                                 synthetic

wood

(4 marks)

Water

1   Water that is safe to drink is called potable water.

(a) Why is potable water not pure?

    ....

    .... **(1 mark)**

(b) In the UK most potable water comes from rainwater that collects in the ground and in lakes and
     rivers. Give the two main steps used to treat groundwater to make it potable. Give a reason for
     each step.

    step 1

    ....

    ....

    step 2

    ....

    .... **(4 marks)**

(c) In the UK, 1.5% of the water requirement is produced by the Thames Water desalination plant.

    (i)   What is desalination?

        .... **(1 mark)**

    (ii) Name **two** methods of
          desalination.

          One of these requires the use of membranes.

        ....

        .... **(2 marks)**

    (iii) Why is desalination expensive?

        ....

        .... **(1 mark)**

2   Sewage and agricultural wastewater require removal of organic matter and harmful microbes.
    Sewage treatment includes the different stages shown in the box below.

> **Guided**

┌───┐
│ sedimentation   anaerobic digestion of sewage sludge   screening and grit removal │
└───┘

(a) Place these stages in the order in which they occur.

    1 ....

    2 ....

    3 *anaerobic digestion of sewage sludge*   **(1 mark)**

(b) What is the purpose of screening and grit removal?

    ....

    .... **(1 mark)**

Core practical – Analysis and purification of water

1 Drinking water has been distilled from seawater since at least 200 AD. Distillation involves evaporation and condensation.

The diagram shows the apparatus used by a student to distil salt water.

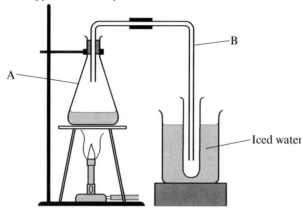

(a) Where does evaporation occur in the apparatus?

.... **(1 mark)**

(b) Where does condensation occur in the apparatus?

.... **(1 mark)**

⟩ Guided ⟩ (c) What is the purpose of the beaker of iced water?

to cool the .... **(1 mark)**

(d) Name the pieces of apparatus A and B.

.... **(1 mark)**

(e) Suggest one piece of equipment that could be used to improve the distillation.

┌───┐
│ This piece of apparatus would mean the iced water is not necessary. │
└───┘

.... **(1 mark)**

(f) Describe a test that could be carried out to show that the water produced is pure. Give the expected result.

....

....

.... **(2 marks)**

(g) What could be added to the water to determine if it contained sulfate ions?

.... **(1 mark)**

(h) Explain why obtaining potable water in this way is not good for the environment.

....

.... **(2 marks)**

Life cycle assessment

1 Why are life cycle assessments carried out on products?

....

....

....

.... **(2 marks)**

2 The table shows data about plastic and glass fizzy drink bottles.

	Energy needed for manufacture in J	Energy needed for filling and delivery in J
Plastic fizzy drink bottle	4 500 000	2 200 000
Glass fizzy drink bottle	7 520 000	2 000 000

(a) How much energy is needed to manufacture a glass fizzy drink bottle?

.... **(1 mark)**

> Guided

(b) Give **three** processes that are considered when creating a life cycle assessment to assess the environmental impact of the plastic and glass fizzy drink bottles.

1. extracting and processing raw materials

2. ....

3. .... **(3 marks)**

(c) Calculate the energy saving when the glass bottle is reused four times compared with using four new plastic bottles.

> First work out the energy to reuse the glass bottle four times, and add the cost of the manufacture. Then work out the cost for manufacturing and filling four plastic bottles.

Energy saving = ... **(5 marks)**

(d) Give **two** methods of reducing the carbon footprint of a plastic bottle.

> Refer to page 85 to remind you about carbon footprints.

....

.... **(2 marks)**

Conserving resources

1   The bar chart shows information about the proportion of different metals that are recycled.

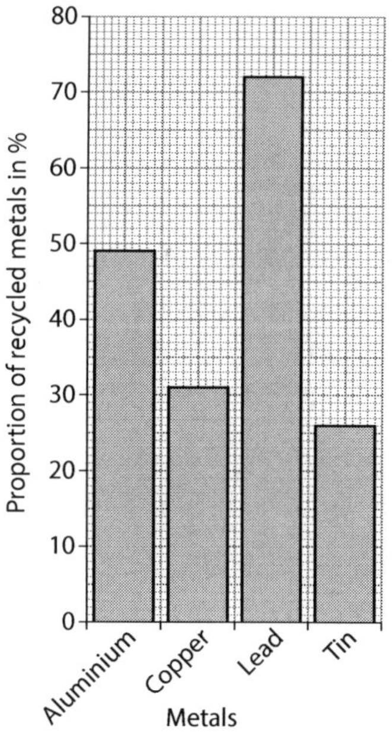

(a) Which **two** metals have the highest proportion recycled?

.... **(1 mark)**

> Guided

(b) Suggest **two** reasons why one metal might be recycled more than another metal.

1. Its ore might be...

2. It might be ....to extract the metal.

(2 marks)

(c) In 2010 the total world lead consumption was approximately 4.6 million tonnes.
Use this information and the data from the chart to calculate the mass of lead recycled that year.
Give your answer to two significant figures.

mass of lead recycled = ... tonnes

(2 marks)

(d) State **three** advantages of recycling metals.

....

....

.... **(3 marks)**

80
70
60
50
40
30
20
10
0

Proportion of recycled metals in %

Aluminium   Copper   Lead   Tin

Metals

| Maths skills | Remember that percentage means out of 100. |

2   Aluminium is extracted from the ore bauxite, which is aluminium oxide.

(a) The formula of aluminium oxide is Al_2O_3. Calculate the relative formula mass of aluminium oxide.

relative atomic masses A_r: O = 16; Al = 27.

.... **(1 mark)**

> Guided

(b) Calculate the percentage of aluminium in aluminium oxide by mass.
Give your answer to three significant figures.

$$\% \text{ aluminium} = \frac{\text{mass of aluminium}}{\text{relative formula mass}} \times 100$$

$$\frac{27 \times 2}{\text{relative formula mass}} \times 100$$

| Remember there are 2 aluminium atoms in aluminium oxide. |

percentage of aluminium = ...%

(2 marks)

(c) In the USA 31% of aluminium metal is recycled. It is melted and reformed into different products.

Why is aluminium recycled?

....

.... **(2 marks)**

Corrosion

1   Many metals corrode (or rust).

(a) What is meant by the term **corrosion**?

....

.... **(1 mark)**

(b) State **two** conditions that are necessary for rusting.

.... **(2 marks)**

(c) Give **two** methods of barrier protection that can be used to prevent corrosion.

....

.... **(2 marks)**

2   Iron can be protected from rusting by sacrificial protection. In an experiment to investigate sacrificial protection, different metals were wrapped around iron nails and left in water for one week.

(a) State **two** ways in which you could ensure that this experiment was a fair test.

> Think about things that must be kept the same in the experiment.

....

.... **(2 marks)**

(b) Explain why rusting occurred in test tube 1.

....

....

.... **(2 marks)**

Guided   (c) Explain why rusting did not occur in test tube 2.

> Use your knowledge of the reactivity series.

The nail would not have rusted in test tube 2 because zinc is more reactive than iron.

....

....

.... **(2 marks)**

(d) Steel is an alloy containing iron. Would the results be the same if steel nails were used?

.... **(1 mark)**

Alloys

1   Because of their range of properties, alloys find many uses in industry and in the home. The diagram shows a typical arrangement of atoms in an alloy.

(a) What is an **alloy**?

.... **(1 mark)**

(b) Which **one** word describes this general structure of metals and alloys?

.... **(1 mark)**

(c) By referring to the above diagram, explain why an alloy is often harder than the pure metal.

....

.... **(2 marks)**

Guided

2   Pure gold is very soft. It is often alloyed with other metals, such as copper or silver, for use in jewellery.

(a) (i)   18 carat gold is an alloy of gold used in jewellery. Calculate the percentage of gold in this alloy.

| Pure gold is 24 carat. |

$$\% \text{ of gold in an alloy } \quad \frac{\text{number of carats}}{24} \times 100 = \text{..................................} \%$$

(2 marks)

(ii) An alloy of gold contains 50% gold. Calculate the number of carats present.

$$\text{number of carats} = 24 \times \frac{50}{100}$$

.... carats   **(2 marks)**

(b) Other common alloys of different metals are shown in the table below. Complete the table to show the elements present in the alloy. Give one use of each alloy.

	Elements present	Use
Brass		
Bronze		
Low carbon steel	iron and carbon	

(3 marks)

Ceramics, polymers, composites

1   Which of the following is used in composites?

Tick **one** box.

☐ borosilicate glass   ☐ poly(ethene)

☐ carbon fibre   ☐ soda lime glass   **(1 mark)**

2   Polymers can be classified as thermosoftening or thermosetting. The diagrams below show the main differences in structure between these polymers.

Thermosoftening   Thermosetting

(a) Describe the difference in properties between thermosoftening and thermosetting polymers.

....

....

.... **(2 marks)**

(b) Should the handles of cooking pots be made from a thermosoftening or a thermosetting polymer? Briefly explain your answer.

....

.... **(2 marks)**

(c) Describe the difference in the structure of a thermosoftening and a thermosetting polymer. Use the diagrams to help.

....

....

....

.... **(2 marks)**

3   Classify the materials as ceramic or polymer.

soda lime glass   ....

pottery   ....

LD poly(ethene)   ....

HD poly(ethene)   ....

borosilicate glass   ....   **(5 marks)**

The Haber process

1 Ammonia is manufactured by the Haber process.

(a) What is the source of nitrogen for the Haber process?

.... **(1 mark)**

(b) What is the source of hydrogen for the Haber process?

.... **(1 mark)**

(c) What is the catalyst used in the Haber process?

Tick **one** box.

☐ cobalt

☐ copper

☐ iron

☐ manganese

(1 mark)

(d) Complete the balanced equation below, including state symbols, for the production of ammonia.

$N_2(g)$ + ... (......) $\rightleftharpoons$ .... (......)   **(2 marks)**

(e) What does the $\rightleftharpoons$ sign tell you about this reaction?

.... **(1 mark)**

(f) What are the conditions of temperature and pressure used in the Haber process?

Tick **one** box.

	Temperature (°C)	**Pressure (atm)**
☐	200	450
☐	200	2
☐	450	200
☐	450	1000

(1 mark)

(g) Why are the gases cooled before ammonia is removed?

.... **(1 mark)**

(h) What happens to the unreacted hydrogen and nitrogen?

.... **(1 mark)**

Fertilisers

1 The diagram below shows the different salts made from ammonia, which are used in the production of NPK fertilisers.

```
                          ammonia
              ┌──────────────┼──────────────┐
       phosphoric acid   sulfuric acid   nitric acid
              │              │              │
              ▼              ▼              ▼
        ┌─────────┐    ┌─────────┐    ┌──────────┐
        │    A    │    │    B    │    │ ammonium │
        │         │    │         │    │  nitrate │
        └─────────┘    └─────────┘    └──────────┘
```

(a) Name products A and B.

A: ....

B: .... **(2 marks)**

(b) Complete the equation for the reaction of ammonia, NH_3, with hydrochloric acid, HCl.

$NH_3 + HCl \rightarrow$ .... **(1 mark)**

(c) (i) Calculate the relative formula mass of ammonium nitrate, NH_4NO_3.

> You will need to refer to the periodic table on page 116 for the relative atomic masses.

.... **(1 mark)**

(ii) Using your answer to (c) (i), calculate the percentage of nitrogen, by mass, in ammonium nitrate, NH_4NO_3.

$$\% \text{ nitrogen} = \frac{\text{mass of nitrogen}}{\text{relative formula mass}} \times 100$$

.... **(2 marks)**

(d) The salts produced in the diagram are used to produce NPK fertilisers.

(i) Explain what fertilisers are used for.

....

.... **(1 mark)**

(ii) What is an NPK fertiliser?

....

.... **(1 mark)**

2 Why is phosphate rock not used directly as a fertiliser?

Tick **one** box.

☐ It is covalently bonded.

☐ It is too expensive.

☐ It does not contain the correct elements.   **(1 mark)**

☐ It is insoluble.

Extended response – Using resources

Describe the industrial production of ammonia by the Haber process.

> You need to include the name and source of each raw material, a balanced symbol equation and any conditions for the reaction.

....

....

....

....

....

....

....

....

....

....

....

....

....

....

....

....

....

....

....

....

....

....

....

....

(6 marks)

Timed Test 1

Time allowed: 1 hour 45 minutes

Total marks: 100

AQA publishes official Sample Assessment Material on its website. This practice exam paper has been written to help you practise what you have learned and may not be representative of a real exam paper.

1 This question is about bonding and structure.

(a) Draw **one** line from each statement to the correct diagram.

Statement   **Structure**

The substance is ionic.

The substance is ammonia NH_3.

The substance is a polymer.

The substance is a metal.

(4 marks)

(b) The figure below shows the structure of an element.

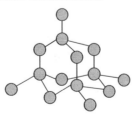

What is the name of this element?

☐ calcium   ☐ oxygen

☐ carbon   ☐ phosphorus   **(1 mark)**

(c) Which statement is true about the element in the above figure?

☐ It has delocalised electrons.   ☐ It has ionic bonds.

☐ It has weak forces between the atoms. ☐ It does not conduct electricity.   **(1 mark)**

(d) The figure below shows a section of the structure of quartz which contains silicon and oxygen atoms.

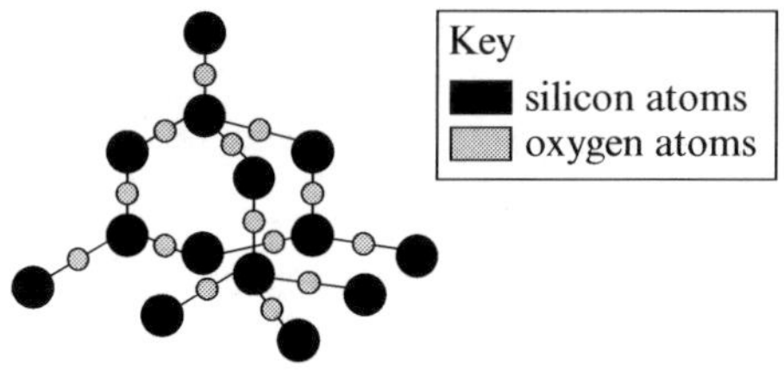

Key
■ silicon atoms
▦ oxygen atoms

Calculate the percentage of silicon atoms in this structure.   **(2 marks)**

(e) Which of the following is a compound?

☐ brass   ☐ methane

☐ chlorine   ☐ sodium chloride solution   **(1 mark)**

(f) The circles in the figure below show atoms.

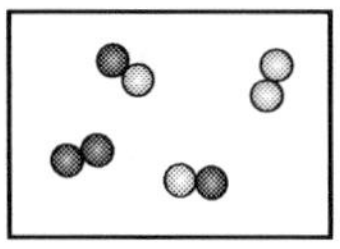

What does the figure represent?

☐ a mixture of an element and two compounds

☐ a mixture of a compound and two elements

☐ a mixture of three different elements made of pairs of atoms

☐ a mixture of three different compounds   **(1 mark)**

(g) What is the best method of separating sand from a mixture of sand and seawater?

☐ chromatography   ☐ filtration

☐ crystallisation   ☐ fractional distillation   **(1 mark)**

(Total for Question 1 is 11 marks)

2 A student investigated the reactivity of three different metals.

This is the method used.

1. Pour 25 cm³ of copper sulfate solution into a beaker.
2. Measure and record the temperature of the solution.
3. Add 0.5 g of metal to the copper sulfate solution.
4. Measure and record the highest temperature reached.
5. Repeat using a different metal.

The results are shown in the table.

	Magnesium	Silver	Zinc
Initial temperature in °C	21	21	20
Highest temperature in °C	40	21	37

(a) What is the dependent variable in the investigation?

☐ mass of metal   ☐ temperature

☐ volume of copper sulfate solution   ☐ type of metal   **(1 mark)**

(b) The box contains the names of some pieces of apparatus.

balance   measuring cylinder   pipette   ruler   thermometer   spatula   gas syringe

   Choose your answer from the box.

   Which piece of apparatus is used to measure

   (i) the mass of metal?   **(1 mark)**

   (ii) the temperature?   **(1 mark)**

(c) Complete the word equation

   magnesium + copper sulfate →   **(2 marks)**

(d) Give **one** observation for the reaction between magnesium and copper sulfate. **(1 mark)**

(e) Which metal does not react with copper sulfate?   **(1 mark)**

(f) Use the results shown in the table to place copper, magnesium, silver and zinc in order
   of reactivity starting with the most reactive.   **(2 marks)**

(g) Suggest **one** reason why the student would not use potassium in this experiment. **(1 mark)**

(h) Give **two** variables the student should control so that the investigation is a fair test. **(2 marks)**

(i) Which metal is extracted from its ore by reduction with carbon?

☐ gold   ☐ potassium   ☐ magnesium   ☐ iron   **(1 mark)**

(j) Aluminium metal reacts with iron(III) oxide.

   (i) Balance the equation for the reaction

         ....Fe_2O_3 + ... Al → .... Fe + ... Al_2O_3 **(1 mark)**

   (ii) Why is the iron(III) oxide reduced in this reaction?   **(2 marks)**

(Total for Question 2 is 16 marks)

3 A student placed 25.0 cm³ of white wine containing tartaric acid and a few drops of bromothymol blue indicator into a conical flask. A titration was carried out to find the volume of sodium hydroxide solution needed to neutralise the tartaric acid found in white wine.

(a) The student carried out four titrations. Her results are shown in the table.

	Titration 1	Titration 2	Titration 3	Titration 4
Volume of NaOH in cm³	20.05	19.45	18.90	19.00

Use the student's concordant results to work out the mean volume of sodium hydroxide added.

(2 marks)

(b) What piece of apparatus is used to add the sodium hydroxide solution to the wine?   **(1 mark)**

(c) Bromothymol blue is yellow in acid and blue in alkali. What is the colour change at the end-point?   **(1 mark)**

(d) State **two** ways in which the student could ensure that the results were accurate in titrations 3 and 4.   **(2 marks)**

(e) Some universal indicator was placed in a beaker of sodium hydroxide solution. The indicator turned blue. What was the pH of the sodium hydroxide solution?

☐ 1   ☐ 5   ☐ 7   ☐ 10   **(1 mark)**

(f) How could the pH of the sodium hydroxide solution be measured more accurately?   **(1 mark)**

(Total for Question 3 is 8 marks)

4 Epsom salts are hydrated magnesium sulfate crystals. Magnesium sulfate crystals can be prepared in the laboratory by reacting magnesium carbonate and sulfuric acid.

The equation for the reaction is:

$$MgCO_3 + H_2SO_4 \rightarrow MgSO_4 + H_2O + CO_2$$

(a) What is observed in this reaction?   **(1 mark)**

*(b) Describe a method for making pure crystals of magnesium sulfate from magnesium carbonate and dilute sulfuric acid.

In your method you should name all the apparatus you will use.   **(6 marks)**

(c) Suggest one safety precaution which should be followed.   **(1 mark)**

(d) The student obtained 1.8 g of magnesium sulfate. The theoretical mass was 2.0 g. Calculate the percentage yield of magnesium sulfate.   **(2 marks)**

(e) Suggest why the yield is less than 100% in this reaction.   **(1 mark)**

(f) The percentage atom economy of a reaction is calculated using the formula:

$$\text{percentage atom economy} = \frac{\text{relative formula mass of desired product from equation}}{\text{sum of relative formula masses of all reactants from equation}} \times 100$$

The equation for the reaction of magnesium carbonate and sulfuric acid is:

$$MgCO_3 + H_2SO_4 \rightarrow MgSO_4 + H_2O + CO_2$$

relative formula masses: $MgCO_3 = 84.0$; $H_2SO_4 = 98.0$; $MgSO_4 = 120.0$

Calculate the percentage atom economy for making magnesium sulfate from magnesium carbonate.

(3 marks)

(Total for Question 4 is 14 marks)

5 The figure below shows the outer electrons in an atom of magnesium and in an atom of chlorine.

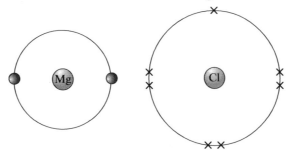

(a) Magnesium and chlorine react to form the ionic compound magnesium chloride.

   (i) Name the type of bonding in magnesium.   **(1 mark)**

   (ii) Name the type of bonding in chlorine molecules, Cl_2.   **(1 mark)**

(b) Describe what happens when an atom of magnesium reacts with two atoms of chlorine. Give your answer in terms of electron transfer. Give the formulae of the ions formed.   **(5 marks)**

(c) Chlorine can also form covalent bonds. Complete the dot-and-cross diagram to show the covalent bonding in a molecule of hydrogen chloride. Show the outer shell electrons only.   **(2 marks)**

(d) Some physical properties of magnesium chloride and hydrogen chloride are shown in the table.

	Magnesium chloride	Hydrogen chloride
Melting point in °C	714	−114
Electrical conductivity	conducts when molten or when in solution	does not conduct

   (i) Which statement is true?

   ☐ Magnesium chloride has a low melting point as it has strong ionic bonds.

   ☐ Magnesium chloride has a high melting point as it has strong covalent bonds.

   ☐ Hydrogen chloride has a low melting point as it has weak covalent bonds.

   ☐ Hydrogen chloride has a low melting point as it has weak intermolecular forces.   **(1 mark)**

   (ii) Which statement is true?

   ☐ Magnesium chloride solid conducts electricity at room temperature.

   ☐ Hydrogen chloride is a liquid at room temperature.

   ☐ Magnesium chloride conducts electricity when in solution as the ions can move and carry charge.

   ☐ Hydrogen chloride conducts electricity when it is a liquid.   **(1 mark)**

(e) Hydrogen chloride dissolves in water and produces H^+ and Cl^- ions.

Name the ions produced.   **(2 marks)**

(f) What is the radius of an atom?

☐ 1×10^{-1} m   ☐ 1×10^{-10} m

☐ 1×10^{-8} m   ☐ 1×10^{-14} m   **(1 mark)**

(Total for Question 5 is 14 marks)

6 An experiment was carried out to find out if the reaction between hydrochloric acid and sodium hydroxide was exothermic.

This is the method used:

1. 25 cm³ of dilute hydrochloric acid was measured out and poured into a polystyrene cup.

2. The temperature of the hydrochloric acid was measured and recorded.

3. 25 cm³ of dilute sodium hydroxide solution was then added gradually in 5 cm³ portions to the hydrochloric acid, stirring after each addition.

4. The temperature of the reaction mixture was measured and recorded.

5. The complete process was repeated.

The table shows the results.

Volume of sodium hydroxide solution added in cm³	0	5	10	15	20	25
Temperature of reaction mixture in °C	20.0	21.5	22.6	23.7	25.2	27.8
Temperature of reaction mixture in °C (repeat)	21.0	21.5	22.4	23.3	25.2	28.2
Mean temperature of reaction mixture in °C	20.5	21.5	22.5	23.5	25.2	

(a) Calculate the mean temperature of the reaction mixture when 25 cm³ of sodium hydroxide was added.   **(1 mark)**

(b) Plot a graph of the results. Draw a line of best fit.

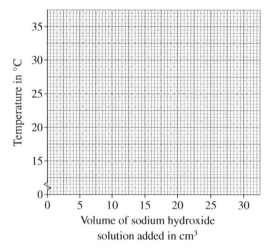

Volume of sodium hydroxide
solution added in cm³   **(3 marks)**

(c) How does your graph show that this reaction was exothermic?   **(1 mark)**

(d) What piece of apparatus could be used to add the sodium hydroxide solution to the acid?

                                                                    (1 mark)

(e) Why might the temperature results recorded be inaccurate? Suggest one improvement which could be made to the experiment.   **(1 mark)**

(f) Complete the chemical equation for the reaction between sodium hydroxide and hydrochloric acid.

NaOH + ... $\rightarrow$ NaCl + ...   **(2 marks)**

(Total for Question 6 is 9 marks)

7 The photograph shows potassium reacting with water.

  (a) How can you tell that a reaction is taking place?
                                      (1 mark)

  (b) What are the products of this reaction?

☐ potassium hydroxide + hydrogen   ☐ potassium oxide + hydrogen

☐ potassium hydroxide + oxygen   ☐ potassium oxide + oxygen   **(1 mark)**

  (c) Which statement is correct?

☐ Each potassium atom loses an electron to form a positive ion.   ☐ Each potassium atom loses an electron to form a negative ion.

☐ Each potassium atom gains an electron to form a positive ion.   ☐ Each potassium atom gains an electron to form a negative ion.   **(1 mark)**

  (d) Potassium reacts with chlorine to form potassium chloride.

    (i) What are the properties of potassium chloride?

☐ coloured solid, soluble in water   ☐ white solid, soluble in water

☐ coloured solid, insoluble in water   ☐ white solid, insoluble in water   **(1 mark)**

    (ii) What are the products of electrolysing molten potassium chloride?

Product at cathode	Product at anode
☐ hydrogen	chlorine
☐ hydrogen	oxygen
☐ potassium	chlorine
☐ potassium	oxygen

                                                    (1 mark)

  (e) (i) The electrolysis of molten lead bromide must be carried out in a fume cupboard. Suggest **one** reason why the electrolysis must be carried out in a fume cupboard.   **(1 mark)**

    (ii) Electrodes are placed into molten lead bromide and connected to a power pack. Suggest one piece of apparatus that could show electricity is flowing in the circuit.   **(1 mark)**

(Total for Question 7 is 7 marks)

8   *This question is about the periodic table and some of its elements.

In 1864, John Newlands arranged all the elements known at the time into a table in order of relative atomic mass. When he did this, he found that each element was similar to the element eight places further on.

This repeating pattern of properties was called the law of octaves but it had problems. For example, iron was in the same group as oxygen and sulphur, which are two non-metals.

(a) Describe how Mendeleev improved on Newland's table and compare Mendeleev's table to the periodic table we use today.   **(6 marks)**

(b) A part of the periodic table is shown below.

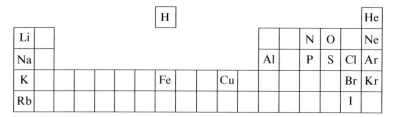

(i)   What is the name of the most reactive element in group 1 and the most reactive element in group 7? Use only the elements shown in the table.

Most reactive in group 1	**Most reactive in group 7**
☐ lithium	bromine
☐ lithium	iodine
☐ rubidium	chlorine
☐ rubidium	iodine

                                                                                         (1 mark)

(ii) Name a coloured, diatomic gas at room temperature and atmospheric pressure, which is present in the periodic table.

☐ bromine   ☐ helium

☐ chlorine   ☐ nitrogen   **(1 mark)**

(iii) Why has does helium have a lower boiling point than argon?

☐ Argon is ionic and helium is covalent.

☐ Argon is less reactive than helium.

☐ The covalent bonds between argon atoms are stronger.

☐ The forces between argon atoms are stronger.   **(1 mark)**

(iv) Name a transition metal in the periodic table.   **(1 mark)**

                                                           (Total for Question 8 is 10 marks)

9 (a) Chlorine has two isotopes. Information about the two isotopes is shown in the table below

Mass number of the isotope	Percentage abundance
35	75.78
37	24.22

Use the information in the table to calculate the relative atomic mass of chlorine. Give your answer to 2 decimal places. **(4 marks)**

(b) An atom of sodium has the symbol $^{23}_{11}$Na.

  (i) Give the number of protons, electrons and neutrons in this atom of sodium. **(3 marks)**

  (ii) Write the electronic structure of sodium. **(1 mark)**

  (iii) Write the formula of the compound formed when sodium and chlorine react. **(1 mark)**

(c) Calculate the relative formula mass (M_r) of the compound $Al(NO_3)_3$.

  relative atomic masses (A_r): oxygen = 16; aluminium = 27; nitrogen = 14 **(2 marks)**

(Total for Question 9 is 11 marks)

(Total = 100)

Timed Test 2

> Time allowed: 1 hour 45 minutes
>
> Total marks: 100
>
> AQA publishes official Sample Assessment Material on its website. This practice exam paper has been written to help you practise what you have learned and may not be representative of a real exam paper.

1 Some substances are pure.

(a) Which statement is always true for a pure substance?

☐ It always boils at 100 °C.   ☐ It has a sharp melting point.

☐ It contains only one type of atom. ☐ It is solid at room temperature.   **(1 mark)**

(b) Which substance is manufactured using sand as a raw material?

☐ polythene   ☐ ceramic

☐ glass   ☐ fertiliser   **(1 mark)**

(c) Which **two** substances are mixtures?

☐ air   ☐ platinum   ☐ sodium chloride

☐ calcium chloride   ☐ paint   **(2 marks)**

(d) Potable water can be produced by desalination of salty water. Which is a method of desalination?

☐ bubbling ozone into the water   ☐ reverse osmosis

☐ filtration   ☐ sedimentation   **(1 mark)**

(e) A student evaporated 50 cm³ of sodium chloride solution to produce sodium chloride crystals. Draw and label a diagram of the apparatus which could be used.   **(3 marks)**

(f) Solder is an alloy of tin and lead.

   (i) A sample of a solder was made by mixing 22.5 g of lead with 15.0 g of tin. Calculate the percentage of tin in this solder.   **(3 marks)**

   (ii) Why are alloys stronger than pure metals?

    ☐ They have stronger bonds between the molecules they contain.

    ☐ They combine the properties of the metals from which they are made.

    ☐ They have atoms of different sizes in their structures.

    ☐ They are made using electrolysis.   **(1 mark)**

(Total for Question 1 is 12 marks)

2 (a) The table shows some tests which were carried out on a solution.

Test	Observation
flame test	lilac flame
6 drops of sodium hydroxide solution were added, followed by excess sodium hydroxide solution.	green precipitate
Some dilute nitric acid and silver nitrate solution were added.	white precipitate

Which three ions were present in the solution? Choose your answer from the box below

| chloride   iron(II)   sulfate   hydrogen   copper   potassium   sodium   calcium |

(3 marks)

   (b) Some dilute hydrochloric acid was added to a sample of sodium carbonate. Describe how you would test for the gas produced.   **(2 marks)**

(Total for Question 2 is 5 marks)

3 Long-chain alkanes can be cracked to form short-chain alkenes. The apparatus in the figure was used to produce ethene.

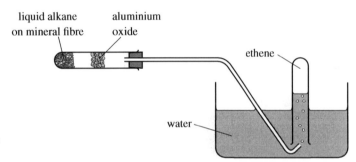

   (a) Which piece of apparatus is missing from the diagram?   **(1 mark)**

   (b) Suggest why the first tube of gas collected should be discarded.   **(1 mark)**

   (c) What is the function of the aluminium oxide?

☐ to catalyse the reaction   ☐ to cause oxidation

☐ to help heat the reaction   ☐ to cause reduction   **(1 mark)**

   (d) Describe a chemical test to distinguish an alkane from an alkene.   **(2 marks)**

   (e) Ethene has the formula C_2H_4.

      (i) What is the formula of hexene, the member of the alkenes homologous series which has 6 carbon atoms?   **(1 mark)**

      (ii) Why is ethene a hydrocarbon?   **(2 marks)**

      (iii) Ethanol can be made industrially from ethene. Complete the word equation.

         ethene + ... $\rightarrow$ ethanol   **(1 mark)**

      (iv) Draw the missing bonds to complete the displayed formula of ethanol.

```
        H       H

H       C       C       O       H

        H       H
```

(1 mark)

(v) Complete the equation for the complete combustion of ethanol.

$C_2H_5OH + 3O_2 \rightarrow 2............ + 3............$ **(2 marks)**

(vi) What is the molecular formula of ethanol?

☐ CH_3O ☐ $C_4H_{10}O_2$

☐ C_2H_6O ☐ CH_2O **(1 mark)**

(Total for Question 3 is 13 marks)

4 A student analysed four different inks using paper chromatography. This is the method used:

1. Draw a pencil line near the bottom of the chromatography paper.

2. Put a spot of blue ink on the start line.

3. Put spots of three separate inks, red, yellow and green, on the start line.

4. Place the bottom of the paper in water and leave it for several minutes.

The figure shows the results.

(a) Why must the start line be drawn in pencil instead of pen?
    (1 mark)

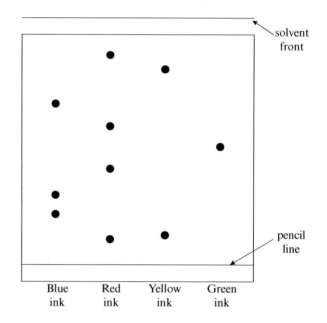

(b) Which ink contains three different components?

☐ blue   ☐ yellow

☐ green   ☐ red   **(1 mark)**

(c) Which mixture contains the most soluble dye?

☐ blue   ☐ yellow

☐ green   ☐ red   **(1 mark)**

(d) Which ink is a pure substance?

☐ blue   ☐ yellow

☐ green   ☐ red   **(1 mark)**

(e) Use the figure above to complete the table showing the distance moved.

Calculate the R_f value for green ink.

	Distance in mm
Distance moved by green ink	
Distance moved from start line to solvent front	

Calculate the R_f value for green ink.

Use the equation: $R_f = \dfrac{\text{distance moved by green ink}}{\text{distance moved by solvent}}$

Give your answer to two significant figures. **(5 marks)**

(Total for Question 4 is 9 marks)

5 A student investigated the reaction of 0.1 g of magnesium ribbon with 50 cm³ of dilute hydrochloric acid at 20°C. The figure shows the apparatus used.

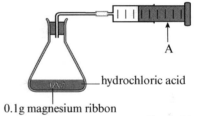

A

hydrochloric acid

0.1g magnesium ribbon

(a) What is A?

☐ measuring cylinder   ☐ gas jar

☐ gas syringe   ☐ graduated pipette **(1 mark)**

(b) Complete the state symbols in the equation.

Mg...... + 2HCl(aq) → MgCl$_2$(aq) + H$_2$..... **(2 marks)**

(c) Give one advantage and one disadvantage of using a measuring cylinder to add the acid to the flask. **(2 marks)**

(d) The table shows the results of this experiment.

Time in s	0	30	60	90	120	150	180
Volume of gas in cm³	0	13	22	30	36	43	49

• Plot these results on the grid.

• Draw a line of best fit.

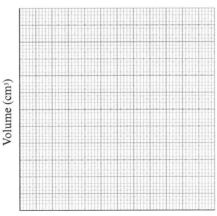

Volume (cm³)

Time (seconds) **(3 marks)**

(e) Use your graph to find the time needed to collect 25 cm³ of gas.   **(1 mark)**

(f) Use your graph to find the volume of gas produced in the first 45 seconds of the reaction. Use this value and the equation:

$$\text{mean rate of reaction} = \frac{\text{volume of gas produced}}{\text{time taken}}$$

Calculate the mean rate of the reaction for the first 45 seconds of the reaction. Give your answer to 1 significant figure.   **(3 marks)**

(g) When the experiment was repeated using more concentrated acid, the rate of reaction increased. Give **two** reasons why.

☐ The particles have a smaller surface area.

☐ There are more particles in the same volume.

☐ The particles have a larger surface area.

☐ The particles have more energy.

☐ There are more collisions which have the activation energy.   **(2 marks)**

(h) Suggest **one** improvement to this experiment.   **(1 mark)**

(i) The student measured the change in volume of the product. Describe another method, other than measuring the change in volume of the product, which the student could have used to find the rate of the reaction between magnesium and hydrochloric acid.   **(2 marks)**

(Total for Question 5 is 17 marks)

6 Ammonia is manufactured by the Haber process.

(a) Balance the equation for the Haber process.

.........N_2 + ...H_2 ⇌ .....NH_3 **(1 mark)**

(b) What does the ⇌ arrow mean?   **(1 mark)**

(c) What is the catalyst used in the Haber process?

☐ copper   ☐ zinc

☐ iron   ☐ manganese   **(1 mark)**

(d) What is the temperature and pressure used in the Haber process?

Temperature in °C	Pressure in atm
☐ 450	2
☐ 450	200
☐ 200	450
☐ 200	2

    (1 mark)

(e) The figure shows how the percentage yield changes with temperature.

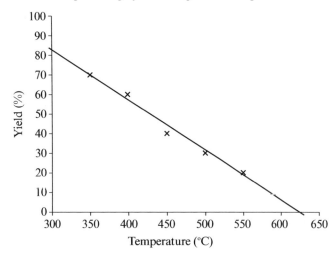

Describe the trend shown in the figure. **(1 mark)**

(f) Ammonia is used to make nitrogen-based fertilisers. The figure shows the consumption of nitrogen fertiliser between 1960 and 2000 in the USA.

(i) Describe the trend shown in the figure.

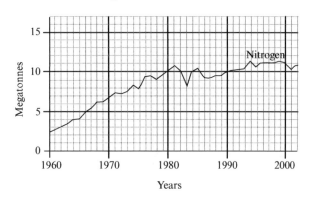

(1 mark)

(ii) A megatonne is 10^6 tonnes. How many tonnes of nitrogen fertiliser were consumed in 1980? Give your answer in standard form. **(2 marks)**

(g) What elements are present in an NPK fertiliser? **(3 marks)**

(h) The figure below shows the effect of some fertilisers on tomato plant growth.

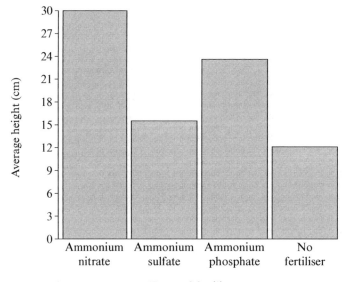

Types of fertiliser

(i) What is the effect of fertiliser on the growth of tomato plants? Use the figure to explain your answer. **(2 marks)**

(ii) Which fertiliser has the greatest effect on tomato plant growth? **(1 mark)**

(iii) Write the formula for ammonium phosphate. **(1 mark)**

(iv) Name the acid which reacts with ammonia to produce ammonium nitrate. **(1 mark)**

(Total for Question 6 is 16 marks)

7　The combustion of fuels is a major source of atmospheric pollutants.

(a) Describe how the different types of atmospheric pollutants are produced as a result of combustion of fuels and give their properties and their environmental impact. **(6 marks)**

(b) Which pollutant gas is produced by the decomposition of vegetation?

☐ carbon monoxide　　　☐ nitrogen oxide

☐ methane　　　　　　　☐ nitrogen dioxide **(1 mark)**

(c) What is a carbon footprint? **(2 marks)**

(d) A carbon footprint can be reduced by reducing emissions of gases. Which gas emissions should be reduced?

☐ carbon dioxide　　　☐ methane　　　☐ hydrogen

☐ sulfur dioxide　　　　☐ nitrogen oxide **(2 marks)**

(Total for Question 7 is 11 marks)

8 The Earth's early atmosphere consisted mainly of carbon dioxide with little or no oxygen gas. Today's atmosphere contains about 21% oxygen gas.

(a) Write the formula of the gas which makes up most of today's atmosphere.   **(1 mark)**

(b) Explain how the amount of oxygen in the atmosphere increased.   **(2 marks)**

(c) Copper powder was heated strongly in a test tube. The figure shows a diagram of the apparatus used. The copper reacted with oxygen in the air in the apparatus. Heating was stopped when there was no further change in the reading on the gas syringe.

copper powder   HEAT   gas syringe

(i) Complete and balance the equation for the reaction which occurs in the test tube.

.......Cu + ...O_2 → ....   **(2 marks)**

(ii) Why should the gas be left for a few minutes before reading the volume left at the end?

☐ Reading the volume while the apparatus is hot is dangerous.

☐ The apparatus must be left to allow the reaction to finish.

☐ The gas must be at room temperature when its volume is measured.

☐ The copper expands when it is hot.   **(1 mark)**

(iii) The table shows the results of the experiment.

Initial volume of gas in syringe	32 cm³
Final volume of gas in syringe	24 cm³

Calculate the percentage decrease in the volume of gas originally in the syringe.   **(3 marks)**

(iv) Compare your answer with the percentage of oxygen in today's atmosphere and suggest why it is different.   **(2 marks)**

(Total for Question 8 is 11 marks)

9 *Rusting is an example of corrosion.

Some students in a class make different predictions:

Air and water are both needed for rusting.

Air only is needed for rusting.

Water only is needed for rusting.

Describe and explain an experiment which the students could carry out to determine if rusting of an iron nail is due to water, water and air, or air alone. State the apparatus and conditions used.

(6 marks)

(Total for Question 9 is 6 marks)

(Total = 100)

The Periodic Table of the Elements

Key

| relative atomic mass |
| atomic symbol |
| name |
| atomic (proton) number |

1	2											3	4	5	6	7	0
																	4 **He** helium 2
7 **Li** lithium 3	9 **Be** beryllium 4											11 **B** boron 5	12 **C** carbon 6	14 **N** nitrogen 7	16 **O** oxygen 8	19 **F** fluorine 9	20 **Ne** neon 10
23 **Na** sodium 11	24 **Mg** magnesium 12											27 **Al** aluminium 13	28 **Si** silicon 14	31 **P** phosphorus 15	32 **S** sulfur 16	35.5 **Cl** chlorine 17	40 **Ar** argon 18
39 **K** potassium 19	40 **Ca** calcium 20	45 **Sc** scandium 21	48 **Ti** titanium 22	51 **V** vanadium 23	52 **Cr** chromium 24	55 **Mn** manganese 25	56 **Fe** iron 26	59 **Co** cobalt 27	59 **Ni** nickel 28	63.5 **Cu** copper 29	65 **Zn** zinc 30	70 **Ga** gallium 31	73 **Ge** germanium 32	75 **As** arsenic 33	79 **Se** selenium 34	80 **Br** bromine 35	84 **Kr** krypton 36
85 **Rb** rubidium 37	88 **Sr** strontium 38	89 **Y** yttrium 39	91 **Zr** zirconium 40	93 **Nb** niobium 41	96 **Mo** molybdenum 42	[98] **Tc** technetium 43	101 **Ru** ruthenium 44	103 **Rh** rhodium 45	106 **Pd** palladium 46	108 **Ag** silver 47	112 **Cd** cadmium 48	115 **In** indium 49	119 **Sn** tin 50	122 **Sb** antimony 51	128 **Te** tellurium 52	127 **I** iodine 53	131 **Xe** xenon 54
133 **Cs** caesium 55	137 **Ba** barium 56	139 **La*** lanthanum 57	178 **Hf** hafnium 72	181 **Ta** tantalum 73	184 **W** tungsten 74	186 **Re** rhenium 75	190 **Os** osmium 76	192 **Ir** iridium 77	195 **Pt** platinum 78	197 **Au** gold 79	201 **Hg** mercury 80	204 **Tl** thallium 81	207 **Pb** lead 82	209 **Bi** bismuth 83	[209] **Po** polonium 84	[210] **At** astatine 85	[222] **Rn** radon 86
[223] **Fr** francium 87	[226] **Ra** radium 88	[227] **Ac*** actinium 89	[261] **Rf** rutherfordium 104	[262] **Db** dubnium 105	[266] **Sg** seaborgium 106	[264] **Bh** bohrium 107	[277] **Hs** hassium 108	[268] **Mt** meitnerium 109	[271] **Ds** darmstadtium 110	[272] **Rg** roentgenium 111	[285] **Cn** copernicium 112	[286] **Uut** ununtrium 113	[289] **Fl** flerovium 114	[289] **Uup** ununpentium 115	[293] **Lv** livermorium 116	[294] **Uus** ununseptium 117	[294] **Uuo** ununoctium 118

1
H
hydrogen
1

* The Lanthanides (atomic numbers 58 – 71) and the Actinides (atomic numbers 90 – 103) have been omitted.

Relative atomic masses for **Cu** and **Cl** have not been rounded to the nearest whole number.

Answers

1. Elements, mixtures and compounds

1 copper (1)

2 (a) C (1) (b) A (1)

3 a substance made up of two or more elements chemically joined together (1)

4 (a) Na (1)

(b) NH_3 (1)

(c) NaOH (1)

5 (a) iron sulfide (1)

(b) An element contains one type of atom only. A compound contains two or more different types of atom. (2)

2. Filtration, crystallisation and chromatography

1 (a) A, crystallisation; B, filtration; C, chromatography (3)

(b) (i) B   (ii) A   (iii) B   (iv) C (4)

2

step 1   addition of water

reason   to dissolve the sodium chloride (1)

step 2   heating and stirring

reason   to speed up dissolving/ensure the salt fully dissolves (1)

step 3   filtration

reason   to separate the insoluble solids from the solution (1)

step 4   crystallisation/evaporation

reason   to remove most of the water (1)

(1 mark for correct order of steps)

3. Distillation

1 distillation (1)

2 (a) 100°C (1)

(b) fractional distillation (1)

3 (a) Distillation (1)

(b) to condense the vapour (1)

(c) evaporation (1)

(d) C fractionating column (1)   D water in (1)   E thermometer (1)

(e) Use an electrical heating mantle. (1)

4. Historical models of the atom

1 (a) positive (1)

(b) electron (1)

(c) The atom has a nucleus which contains protons/positive charge (1) with electrons in the shells (1).

2 (a) nucleus (1)

(b) positive (1)

(c) proton (1)

(d) electron (1)

3 Chadwick (1)

5. Particles in an atom

1 (a) Ca (1)

(b) 20 (1)

2 (a) The sum of the protons and neutrons in an atom is its mass number. (1)

(b) There is an equal number of protons and electrons so the total number of positive charges cancels the total number of negative charges. (1)

(c) 11 protons, 12 neutrons, 11 electrons (3)

(d) protons and neutrons (both needed) (1)

3 (a)

Atom	Atomic number	Mass number	Number of electrons	Number of neutrons	Number of protons
A	27	59	27	59 – 27 = 32	27
B	28	59	28	31	28
C	13	27	13	14	13
D	19	39	19	20	19

(4) (1 for each correct line)

(b) A is cobalt, B is nickel, C is aluminium, D is potassium (4)

6. Atomic structure and isotopes

1 (a)

Particle	Relative mass	Relative charge
electron	very small	–1
neutron	1	0
proton	1	+1

(3) (1 for each correct line)

(b) protons, 19; neutrons, 20; electrons, 19 (3)

(c) 1×10^{-14} m (1)

(d) They have the same number of protons (atomic number) (1), but different numbers of neutrons (mass number) (1).

2 (a) They are atoms with the same atomic number and a different number of neutrons. (1)

(b) $= \dfrac{12 \times 99 + 13 \times 1}{99+1} = 12.01 = 12.0$ (to one decimal place) (2)

7. Electronic structure

1 nitrogen (1)

2 2,8,3 drawn (1) 2,8,7 drawn (1) 2,8,8,2 drawn (1)

3 (a) silicon (1) 14 (1)

(b) 14 of each (1)

(c) mass number (1)

4 (a) 2,8,8,1 **(1)**

(b) 2,8,5 **(1)**

(c) 2,8,8,2 **(1)**

8. Development of the periodic table

1 (a) 7 **(1)**

(b) noble gases/group 0 **(1)**

(c) two elements in one position/copper present/silver present **(1)**

(d) any two from: Mendeleev's table

has gaps **(1)**

has fewer elements **(1)**

has no noble gases **(1)**

is arranged in order of atomic weight not atomic number **(1)**

(e) germanium **(1)**

(f) isotopes **(1)** weight **(1)**

2 atomic weight **(1)**

9. The modern periodic table

1 (a) metal **(1)** metal **(1)** non-metal **(1)**

(b) mercury **(1)**

(c) 2 **(1)** 2 **(1)**

7 **(1)** 7 **(1)**

2 by increasing atomic number **(1)**

3 (a) A and F **(1)**   (b) D **(1)**   (c) E **(1)**

4 (a) They have the same number of electrons in the outer shell of their atoms. **(1)**

(b) The element with the smallest atomic number is boron. The atomic number gives the number of protons, so the element with the lowest number of protons is boron. **(1)**

10. Group 0

1 (a) 2,8 **(1)**

(b) It has a full outer shell and is stable. **(1)**

2 2 **(1)**

3 (a) group 0 **(1)**

(b) approximately –160 (°C) **(1)**

(c) boiling point increases with increasing relative atomic mass **(1)**

(d) approximately 2.5 (g/dm^3) **(1)**

(e) He, 2 **(1)** Ne, 2,8 **(1)**

4 They have a full outer shell and are stable. **(1)**

11. Group 1

1 (a) rubidium **(1)**

(b) potassium **(1)**

(c) sodium **(1)**

2 (a) Their atoms have one electron in the outer shell. **(1)**

(b) (i) Similarities – any two from: metal floats, moves, disappears, bubbles **(2)**

Differences – any two from: potassium: reacts faster/bubbles faster, moves faster (on the surface), melts, produces (lilac/purple) flame **(2)**

(ii) potassium hydroxide and hydrogen gas **(2)**

3 (a) sodium chloride **(1)**

sodium oxide **(1)**

(b) (i) $2Na + 2H_2O \rightarrow 2NaOH + H_2$ **(1)**

(ii) hydroxide ion **(1)**

12. Group 7

1 halogens **(1)**

2 (a) sodium + bromine $\rightarrow$ sodium bromide **(1)**

(b) 7 **(1)**

(c) $2K + Cl_2 \rightarrow 2KCl$ **(1)**

(d) potassium chloride **(1)**

3 (a) Reactivity decreases down the group and so bromine is less reactive than chlorine. It will not displace the more reactive chlorine from the sodium chloride solution. **(2)**

(b) sodium chloride + iodine **(1)**

(c) displacement **(1)**

(d) Reactivity decreases as you go down the group. **(1)**

13. Transition metals

1 chromium **(1)**

2 (a) Like all transition metals iron is a catalyst, forms ions with different charges, and forms coloured compounds in solution. **(3)**

(b) FeO **(1)** Fe_2O_3 **(1)**

3 false

true

false

false **(4)**

4 (a) D **(1)**   (b) A **(1)**   (c) B **(1)**   (d) E **(1)**

14. Chemical equations

1 (a) potassium + chlorine $\rightarrow$ potassium chloride **(1)**

(b) magnesium + oxygen $\rightarrow$ magnesium oxide **(1)**

(c) hydrogen + bromine $\rightarrow$ hydrogen bromide **(1)**

(d) copper + oxygen $\rightarrow$ copper oxide **(1)**

2 (a) One molecule of methane reacts with two molecules of oxygen to produce one molecule of carbon dioxide and two molecules of water. **(2)**

(b) 16 g **(1)**

3 (a) $2Mg + O_2 \rightarrow 2MgO$ **(1)**

(b) $2HCl + Ca \rightarrow CaCl_2 + H_2$ **(1)**

(c) $N_2 + 3H_2 \rightarrow 2NH_3$ **(1)**

(d) $2SO_2 + O_2 \rightarrow 2SO_3$ **(1)**

(e) $H_2 + F_2 \rightarrow 2HF$ **(1)**

4 (a) $4Na + O_2$ **(1)** $\rightarrow 2Na_2O$ **(1)**

(b) $4K + O_2 \rightarrow 2K_2O$ **(2)** (1 mark for symbols, 1 mark for balancing)

5 3 **(1)**

15. Extended response – Atomic structure

Answer could include the following points. **(6)**

Physical properties

- Transition metals have high melting points.
- Alkali metals have low melting points.
- Transition metals have high densities.
- Alkali metals have low densities/are less dense than water.

Chemical properties

- Transition metals have low reactivity/react slowly (with water).

- Alkali metals are very reactive/react quickly (with water).
- Transition metals form ions with different charges, for example iron forms 2+ and 3+ ions.
- The alkali metals all form 1+ ions.

This content is not exhaustive; other creditworthy responses will be awarded marks too.

16. Forming bonds

1 electrostatic forces (**1**)

2 (a) metal: calcium, magnesium (**1**)

   non-metal: chlorine, oxygen, hydrogen, sulfur, nitrogen (**1**)

   (b) ionic: calcium oxide (**1**), magnesium chloride (**1**)

   covalent: hydrogen chloride (**1**), hydrogen sulfide (**1**)

3 (a) NH_3 (**1**)

   (b) covalent (**1**) sharing of electrons between atoms (**1**)

   (c) metallic (**1**)

4 nitrogen and hydrogen (**1**)

17. Ionic bonding

1 2– (**1**)

2 (a) 2,8,1 (**1**)

   (b) 2,8 (**1**)

3 Each chlorine atom gains one electron. (**1**)

4 Two sodium atoms each lose one electron (**1**), forming Na^+ ions (**1**). The electrons are transferred from sodium to oxygen (**1**). Each oxygen atom gains 2 electrons (**1**), forming O^{2-} ions (**1**).

18. Giant ionic lattices

1 usually dissolve in water (**1**)

   high melting point (**1**)

2 six chloride ions (**1**)

3 (a) ionic (**1**)

   (b) giant ionic lattice (**1**)

   (c) It shows there are gaps between the ions but in the crystal the ions are touching. (**1**)

   (d) electrostatic attraction (**1**) between oppositely charged ions (**1**)

   (e) The ions are held tightly in the lattice (**1**) and cannot move and carry charge (**1**).

19. Covalent bonding

1 (a) B (**1**)

   (b) A (**1**)

   (c) C (**1**)

   (d) water (**1**)

2

   (**2**)

3 (a) (i) The lone pair is 'XX'. (**1**)

      (ii) The covalent bond is any 'OX'. (**1**)

   (b) PH_3 (**1**)

   (c) compound (**1**)

   (d) shared pair of electrons (**1**)

20. Small molecules

1 (a) covalent (**1**)

   (b) It does not conduct electricity (**1**) as the molecules do not have an overall electric charge/there are no charged particles free to move (**1**).

2 (a) (i) CCl_4 (**1**) (ii) HCl (**1**)

   (b)

   (**1**)

3

   (**1**)

4 The forces between the molecules are weak. (**1**)

21. Polymer molecules

1 (a) a large molecule made of repeating units, linked by covalent bonds (**1**)

   (b) carbon (**1**) fluorine (**1**)

   (c) covalent (**1**)

2

   (**1**)

3 large; atoms; strong; strong (**4**)

4 (a) a large number (**1**)

   (b) covalent bond (**1**)

   (c) solid (**1**)

22. Diamond and graphite

1 carbon (**1**)

2 It has no free electrons or ions. (**1**)

3 simple molecular, simple molecular, giant covalent, giant covalent, simple molecular (**5**)

4 A: carbon atom, B: covalent bond, C: intermolecular force (**3**)

23. Graphene and fullerenes

1 Graphene is a single layer of graphite. (**1**)

   Graphene has hexagonal rings of carbon. (**1**)

2 graphene (**1**)

3 (a) any two from: 5 (**1**) 6 (**1**) 7 (**1**)

   (b) carbon nanotubes and buckminsterfullerene (**2**)

4 (a) carbon nanotubes (**1**)

   (b) good, high (**2**)

24. Metallic bonding

1 (a) in layers (**1**)

   (b) delocalised (**1**)

2 (a) It has layers of positive ions (**1**) with delocalised electrons (**1**).

   (b) It is the electrostatic attraction (**1**) between the positive metal ions and the delocalised electrons (**1**).

3 (a) (i) metallic (**1**)   (ii) ionic (**1**)

(b) good thermal conductor/shiny when freshly cut (**1**)

25. Giant metallic structures and alloys

1 (a) (i) can be hammered into shape (**1**)

(ii) It contains delocalised electrons. (**1**)

(iii) protons 79 (**1**) neutrons 118 (**1**)

(b) In an alloy there are different sizes of atoms present (**1**). This makes it difficult for the layers of atoms to slide over each other (**1**).

2 % = 9/37 (**1**) × 100 = 24% (**1**)

26. The three states of matter

1 W gas (**1**)

X solid (**1**)

Y solid (**1**)

Z liquid (**1**)

2 (a) A melting (**1**)

B evaporation (**1**)

C condensation (**1**)

D freezing (**1**)

(b) The particles gain energy and vibrate faster (**1**). They overcome the forces between them and move apart and form a liquid (**1**).

27. Nanoscience

1 atom, nanoparticle, fine particle, coarse particle (**1**)

2 (a) a particle between 1 and 100 nm in size (**1**)

(b) Compared with the particles in ordinary powders, nanoparticles have a surface area that is very large (**1**).

3 (a) Nanoparticles may have properties different from those for the same materials in bulk because of their high surface area to volume ratio (**1**). Smaller quantities are needed to be effective than for materials with normal particle sizes (**1**).

(b) large surface area (**1**)

(c) We still do not know the risks involved (**1**).

28. Extended response – Bonding and structure

Answer could include the following points. (**6**)

- Metals have giant structures with strong metallic bonds,
- which take much energy to break so they have high melting points.
- They are good conductors of electricity because the delocalised electrons in the metal
- move and carry electrical charge.
- They are good conductors of heat because the thermal energy is carried by the delocalised electrons.
- The layers of ions are able to slide over each other,
- but they are held in the structure by the attraction of the electrons and ions. Hence copper is soft and malleable.

This content is not exhaustive; other creditworthy responses will be awarded marks too.

29. Relative formula mass

1 Cl: 2 × 35.5 = 71 (**1**)

HF: 1 + 19 = 20 (**1**)

NaOH: 23 + 16+ 1 = 40 (**1**)

K₂O: 39 × 2 + 16 = 94 (**1**)

2 (a) 62 (**1**) (b) 342 (**1**) (c) 88 (**1**) (d) 98 (**1**)

(e) 164 (**1**) (f) 342 (**1**)

30. Balanced equations and masses

1 (a) (i) sodium hydrogen carbonate + citric acid → sodium citrate + carbon dioxide + water (**1**)

(ii) carbon dioxide gas (**1**)

(b) (i)

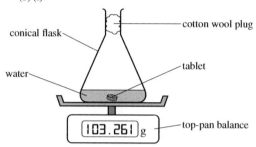

(**3 if all correct, 2 marks if one label missing, 1 mark if two labels missing**)

(ii) A gas was lost from the flask. (**1**)

2

Reactant	Relative formula mass	Product	Relative formula mass
CuCO₃	123.5	CuCl₂	134.5
HCl	36.5	H₂O	18
		CO₂	44

(5)

total formula mass of reactants = 123.5 + (2 × 36.5) = 196.5 (**1**)

total formula mass of products = 134.5 + 18 + 44 = 196.5 (**1**)

31. Concentration of a solution

1 D (**1**)

2 (a) volume = 2500/1000 = 2.5 dm³ (**1**)

(b) 0.5 dm³ (**1**)

(c) 0.025 dm³ (**1**)

3 (a) 25 g/dm³ (**1**)

(b) 36.5 g/dm³ (**1**)

(c) 5 g/dm³ (**1**)

4 concentration = (10/250) × 1000 = 40 g/dm³ (**1**)

5 16 g/dm³ (**1**)

6 (a) mixture of a solute and water/solution in which the solvent is water (**1**)

(b) 100 g (**1**)

32. Reaction yields

1 (a) 0.8 g (**1**)   (b) 1.0 g (**1**)   (c) Little product would escape. (**1**)

2 (a) CuCO₃(s) + 2HNO₃(aq) → Cu(NO₃)₂(aq) + H₂O(l) + CO₂(g) (**3**) (**1 mark for each correct state symbol**)

(b) % = 8/15 × 100 = 53.3333 = 53.3% to 1 decimal place (**2**)

(c) Some of the product may be lost during separation, e.g. in filtration (**1**). Not all copper nitrate crystallises/some stays in solution (**1**).

33. Atom economy

1 (a)

Reactant	Relative formula mass	Product	Relative formula mass
NaOH	40	NaCl	58.5
HCl	36.5	H_2O	18

(4)

(b) % = 58.5/(36.5 + 40) (**1**) × 100 = 58.5/76.5 × 100 (**1**) = 76.5% (**1**)

2 (a) 4/48 (**1**) × 100 (**1**) = 8.3% (**1**)

(b) If a use could be found for the carbon dioxide, then the atom economy would increase to 100%. (**1**)

3 (a) % = 28/142 (**1**) = 19.7% (**1**)

(b) 100% (**1**)

34. Reactivity series

1 (a) zinc, iron, copper (**1**)

(b) Blue colour fades (**1**) OR red brown solid is produced (**1**).

2 (a) magnesium hydroxide + hydrogen (**1**)

(b) calcium nitrate + hydrogen (**1**)

(c) zinc chloride + hydrogen (**1**)

3 (a) hydrogen (**1**)   (b) potassium hydroxide (**1**)

(c) any two from: heat, potassium disappears, lilac flame, bubbles, moves on surface (**2**)

4 calcium, magnesium, zinc, copper (**1**)

35. Oxidation, reduction and the extraction of metals

1 gain of oxygen (**1**)

2 (a) silver (**1**)

(b) any two from: magnesium, tin, calcium (**2**)

(c) carbon (**1**)

(d) any one from: calcium, magnesium (**1**)

3 (a) They are very unreactive. (**1**)

(b) (i) $2Fe_2O_3 + 3C \rightarrow 4Fe + 3CO_2$ (**1**)

(ii) Fe_2O_3 (**1**)

(iii) CO has been oxidised because it has gained oxygen (**1**) and formed CO_2 (**1**).

36. Reactions of acids

1 neutralisation (**1**)

2 (a) base (**1**)

(b) magnesium chloride, aluminium chloride (**2**)

3

Acid	Base	Salt
hydrochloric acid	lithium hydroxide	lithium chloride
nitric acid	calcium oxide	calcium nitrate
sulfuric acid	sodium hydroxide	sodium sulfate
hydrochloric acid	magnesium oxide	magnesium chloride

(4)

4 (a) magnesium (**1**)

(b) potassium sulfate (**1**)

(c) carbon dioxide (**1**)

(d) copper sulfate (**1**)

37. Core practical – Salt preparation

1 (a) blue (**1**)

(b) from top: filter funnel, filter paper, residue/copper carbonate, filtrate/copper sulfate solution (**2**)

(c) Heat the filtrate to evaporate some of the water, and crystals start to form (**1**). Leave to cool and crystallise (**1**).

2 (a) sodium sulfate (**1**)

(b) Sodium is too reactive (**1**) and the reaction would be too violent (**1**).

3 Measure out some dilute hydrochloric acid into a beaker. Add a spatula measure of cobalt oxide, with stirring (**1**). Filter (to remove excess cobalt oxide) (**1**). Heat the filtrate to evaporate some of the water, and crystals start to form (**1**). Leave to cool and crystallise (**1**).

38. The pH scale

1 (a) any two from: Add some universal indicator (**1**); compare to colour chart (**1**); use a pH meter (**1**); record to 1 decimal place (**1**).

(b) C (**1**)

(c) A and B (**1**)

(d) E (**1**)

(e) An aqueous solution is one where the solute is dissolved in water. (**1**)

(f) hydrogen ion (**1**) hydroxide ion (**1**)

2 (a) sulfuric acid + potassium hydroxide → potassium sulfate + water (**1**)

(b) A reaction between hydrogen ions and hydroxide ions to produce water. (**1**)

(c) green (**1**)

39. Core practical – Titration

1 (a) A = burette (**1**)

B = conical flask (**1**)

C = white tile (**1**)

(b) (graduated or volumetric) pipette (**1**)

(c) to help see the indicator change clearly (**1**)

(d) it changes from yellow to red (**2**) (**1 mark only if wrong way round**)

(e) (i) 27.20 (**1**), 26.75 (**1**), 26.05 (**1**), 26.15 (**1**)

(ii) (26.05 + 26.15)/2 = 26.10 (**2**)

40. Extended response – Quantitative chemistry

Answer could include the following points. (**6**)

- Use a pipette to measure out 25.0 cm^3 of sodium hydroxide solution. (**1**)
- Pour into a conical flask. (**1**)
- Add drops of phenolphthalein/methyl orange/litmus to the conical flask. (**1**)
- Swirl flask. (**1**)
- Add dilute sulfuric acid from a burette (**1**)

- until indicator changes from colourless to pink/yellow to red/blue to red. **(1)**
- Repeat until concordant results achieved. **(1)**
- Add the acid dropwise at the endpoint. **(1)**

This content is not exhaustive; other creditworthy responses will be awarded marks too.

41. Electrolysis

1 (a) Lamp would light. **(1)**

(b) Solid lead bromide does not conduct as the ions cannot move and carry charge **(1)**. When molten the ions can move and carry charge **(1)**.

(c) anode: bromine **(1)** cathode: lead **(1)**

(d) good conductor of electricity **(1)** inert/does not react **(1)**

2 (a) anode: chlorine **(1)** cathode: sodium **(1)**

(b) It does not decompose/no products form **(1)** as the ions cannot move and it does not conduct **(1)**.

(c) Metal ions are positive **(1)** and move to the negative cathode **(1)**.

42. Aluminium extraction

1 (a) Aluminium ion moves to cathode. **(1)**

Oxide ion moves to anode. **(1)**

(b) Al_2O_3 **(1)**

2 (a) The ions can move when molten **(1)** and carry a charge **(1)**.

(b) to lower the melting point, and so it is more economical **(1)**

(c) Aluminium ions are positive and they move to the negative electrode **(1)**, where they discharge and gain electrons and are reduced, forming aluminium **(1)**.

(d) oxygen, carbon dioxide **(2)**

(e) cathode **(1)**

(f) Oxygen is formed at the anode **(1)** and it reacts with the carbon **(1)** anode to produce carbon dioxide **(1)**.

43. Electrolysis of solutions

1 It contains ions which can move **(1)**.

2 hydrogen bromine **(1)**

3 (a) (i) hydrogen **(1)** (ii) oxygen **(1)**

(b)

Electrolyte solution	Anode	Cathode
copper chloride	chlorine	copper
potassium bromide	bromine	hydrogen
sodium iodide	iodine	hydrogen
sodium sulfate	oxygen	hydrogen

(4) (1 mark per row)

44. Core practical – Electrolysis

1 (a) A, cathode **(1)**, B, anode **(1)**, graphite **(1)**

(b) solute: potassium chloride **(1)** solvent: water **(1)**

(c) potassium chloride: cathode, hydrogen **(1)** anode, chlorine **(1)**

calcium nitrate: test, relights a glowing splint **(1)** cathode, hydrogen **(1)** anode, oxygen **(1)**

sulfuric acid: cathode, hydrogen **(1)** anode, oxygen **(1)**

zinc bromide: anode, bromine **(1)**

silver nitrate: anode, oxygen **(1)**

(d) Carry out in a fume cupboard – chlorine is toxic. **(2)**

45. Extended response – Chemical changes

Answer could include the following points. **(6)**

- calcium chloride formed in both
- Water is other product in reaction of calcium hydroxide with hydrochloric acid.
- Hydrogen is other product in reaction of calcium with hydrochloric acid.
- observations for calcium hydroxide and hydrochloric acid – solution remains colourless
- observations for calcium and hydrochloric acid
- bubbles/effervescence
- Solid disappears.
- colourless solution formed
- $Ca(OH)_2 + 2HCl \rightarrow CaCl_2 + H_2O$
- $Ca + 2HCl \rightarrow CaCl_2 + H_2$

This content is not exhaustive; other creditworthy responses will be awarded marks too.

46. Exothermic reactions

1

Initial temperature in °C	Final temperature in °C	Temperature change in °C
21	26	increased by 5
21	–5	decrease by 26
21	36	increase by 15

(6)

2 (a) The amount of energy in the Universe at the end of a chemical reaction is the same **(1)** as before the reaction takes place **(1)**.

(b) If a reaction transfers energy to the surroundings the products must have less energy than the reactants, by the amount transferred. **(1)**

3 (a) An exothermic reaction is one that transfers energy to the surroundings **(1)** so the temperature of the surroundings increases **(1)**.

(b) handwarmers **(1)** and self-heating cans **(1)**

4 (a) $CH_4 + 2O_2 \rightarrow CO_2 + 2H_2O$ **(1)**

(b) increases **(1)**

47. Endothermic reactions

1 (a) gives out **(1)** takes in **(1)**

(b) Place a thermometer in **(1)**; temperature drops **(1)**.

(c) any one from: thermal decomposition **(1)** citric acid and sodium hydrogen carbonate **(1)** photosynthesis **(1)**

2 The equation states that energy is given out in the reaction of glucose with oxygen **(1)**. Hence energy is taken in in the reverse reaction (photosynthesis) meaning it is endothermic **(1)**.

3 (a) A – exothermic **(1)** B – endothermic **(1)** C – exothermic **(1)** D – endothermic **(1)**

(b) +29 **(1)** –11 **(1)**

48. Core practical – Energy changes

1 (a) sodium hydroxide + hydrochloric acid → sodium chloride + water (**1**)

(b) Polystyrene cup is a poor conductor of heat and so no energy is lost to the surroundings. (**1**)

(c) to ensure the two solutions mix completely and fully react (**1**)

(d) Add a lid (**1**) to reduce heat loss (**1**).

(e) (i) exothermic (**1**) the temperature increased (**1**)

(ii) type of acid (**1**)

(iii) one from: volume of acid (**1**) volume of sodium hydroxide (**1**)

49. Activation energy

1 y (vertical) axis – Energy (**1**); x (horizontal) axis – Progress of reaction (**1**)

(b) A (**1**)

(c) C (**1**)

(d) exothermic (**1**)

2 reaction 1, endothermic (**1**) reaction 2, exothermic (**1**) reaction 3, exothermic (**1**)

3 (a) It is the energy needed for a reaction to occur. (**1**)

(b) collide with sufficient energy (to overcome the activation energy) (**1**)

50. Cells

1 (a) hydrogen + oxygen → water (**1**)

(b) hydrogen fuel cell, the only waste product is water (**1**); rechargeable cell, portable (**1**)

(c) two different metals (**1**) in contact with an electrolyte (**1**)

(d) to give a higher voltage (**1**)

(e) Chemical reactions are reversed when an external electrical current is supplied. (**1**)

2 (a) B, A and D are more reactive than copper because the voltage observed is positive for B, A and D (**1**), with B more reactive than A and D. C is less reactive than copper (**1**), so the order is B, A, D, copper, C (**1**).

(b) 0 V (**1**)

(c) ammonium chloride solution (**1**)

51. Extended response – Energy changes

(a) Cells contain chemicals which react to produce electricity (**1**). Fuel cells are supplied by an external source of fuel (e.g. hydrogen) and oxygen or air (**1**).

(b) Rechargeable cells and batteries can be recharged because the chemical reactions are reversed when an external electrical current is supplied (**1**). In non-rechargeable cells and batteries the chemical reactions stop when one of the reactants has been used up (**1**).

(c) advantages and disadvantages of chemical cells; any two from: (**2**)

- portable
- Rechargeable cells can be reused.
- When one of the reactants in a non-rechargeable cell runs out, the chemical reactions stop.
- difficult to dispose of

advantages and disadvantages of fuel cells; any two from: (**2**)

- constant voltage
- do not run down if fuel is continuously supplied

- only waste product of hydrogen fuel cell is water
- not portable

52. Rate of reaction

1 time taken = 2 × 60 = 120 seconds

rate = change/time = 1.2/120 (**1**)

mean rate of reaction = 0.01 g/s (**1**)

2 (a) (i) rate = change/time = (0.36 − 0.22)/(4 − 2) = 0.14/2 (**1**)

rate of reaction = 0.07 g/min (**1**)

(ii) rate = change/time = (0.42 − 0.36)/(6 − 4) = 0.06/2 (**1**)

rate of reaction = 0.03 g/min (**1**)

(b) conical flask on balance (**1**) acid and calcium carbonate in flask (**1**) cotton wool (**1**)

53. Rate of reaction on a graph

1 (a) magnesium + hydrochloric acid →

magnesium chloride + hydrogen (**1**)

(b) axes labelled with sensible scales (**1**), all points from table plotted taking up more than half the grid (**1**) and a smooth curve drawn (**1**).

2 (a) experiment A, 30 cm³ (**1**) experiment B, 16 cm³ (**1**)

(b) 58 (**1**) 29 (**1**) 58 − 29 = 28 cm³ (**1**)

(c) (i) 24 (**1**)

(ii) 24/40 (**1**) = 0.6 (**1**)

54. Collision theory

1 when particles collide with sufficient energy (**1**)

2 (a) any two from:

Rate is fast at start. (**1**)

Rate slows down. (**1**)

When graph is horizontal rate is zero. (**1**)

(b) The particles have more energy (**1**). The particles move faster (**1**).

(c) The rate of reaction would have increased. The acid was more concentrated so there were more particles (**1**) in the same volume (**1**) so there were more frequent collisions/more collisions per second (**1**) and a faster rate of reaction (**1**).

55. Rate: pressure, surface area

1 There are more particles in the same volume and there are more collisions. (**1**)

2 calcium carbonate powder reacting with concentrated nitric acid (**1**)

3 (a) 45 s (**1**)

(b) A (**1**); it has a steeper slope as it is a faster reaction (due to a larger surface area of metal) but the same volume of gas is produced (**1**).

(c)

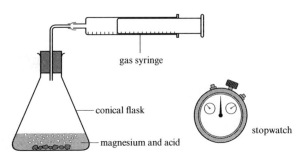

gas syringe

conical flask

magnesium and acid

stopwatch

56. Rate: temperature

1 (a) Increasing the temperature makes the reaction rate increase. (**1**)

(b) magnesium chloride (**1**) hydrogen (**1**)

2 (a) (i) flask A (**1**)

(ii) least reactive metal (**1**)
lowest temperature (**1**)

(b) (i) E and F (**1**)

(ii) any two from: same concentration (**1**), same volume of acid (**1**), same mass of magnesium (**1**), same surface area/volume ratio (**1**)

3 There are more frequent collisions as the particles have more energy. (**1**)

57. Core practical – Rate of reaction

(a) stopwatch (**1**)

(b) bubbles (**1**) magnesium disappears (**1**)

(c) The temperature (**1**) and the volume (**1**) of the hydrochloric acid must be kept the same in all experiments.

(d) A (**1**)

(e) A (**1**)

(f) the result at 8 minutes for C (**1**)

(g) Place magnesium and acid on balance and record mass (**1**). Record mass every minute until reaction stops (**1**). Plot a graph of mass lost against time and gradient is rate (**1**).

58. Catalysts

1
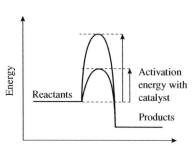

(4) (1 mark for each correct label)

2 (a) gas syringe (**1**)

(b) (i) 48 cm^3 (**1**)

(ii) zinc oxide (**1**) reaction takes most time (**1**)

(iii) The line should start at (0,0) and remain steeper and above the graph line, but level off earlier and to the same volume. (**1**)

59. Reversible reactions

1 A reaction in which the products of the reaction can react to produce the original reactants. (**1**)

2 (a) $N_2 + 3H_2 \rightleftharpoons 2NH_3$ (**2**)

(b) $\rightleftharpoons$/double arrow (**1**)

3 (a) This means the reaction goes in both directions. (**1**)

(b) carbon monoxide, hydrogen, methane, water (**2**) (**1 mark for any three**)

4 (a) reverse (right to left) direction (**1**)

(b) white (**1**) to blue (**1**)

(c) contains water (**1**)

60. Equilibrium

1 (a) Equilibrium is reached when the forward and reverse reactions (**1**) occur at exactly the same rate (**1**).

(b) The apparatus must be sealed /prevent the escape of reactants and products/a closed system must be used. (**1**)

2 (a) Increasing the pressure increases the yield. (**1**)

(b) Increasing the temperature decreases the yield. (**1**)

(c) 40% (**1**)

(d) reversible (**1**)

61. Extended response – Rates of reaction

Answer could include the following points. (**6**)

• Add magnesium to acid.

• Time reaction until magnesium disappears or measure volume of gas, per minute.

• Change concentration and repeat at several different concentrations.

• Repeat experiment for reliability.

• same mass of magnesium

• same surface area of magnesium

• same volume acid

• same temperature

This content is not exhaustive; other creditworthy responses will be awarded marks too.

62. Crude oil

1 mixture (**1**)

2 (a) $C_{11} - C_{13}$ (**1**)

(b) (i) residue (**1**)

(ii) petrol (**1**)

(c) fractional distillation (**1**)

(d) the higher the number of carbon atoms, the higher the boiling point range (**1**)

(e) (i) any two from: fuel oil (**1**), kerosene (**1**), diesel oil (**1**), gasoline (**1**) fuel gases (**1**)

(ii) any three from: solvents (**1**), lubricants (**1**), polymers (**1**), detergents (**1**), fuels (**1**)

63. Alkanes

1 (a) a compound made up of hydrogen and carbon atoms (**1**) only (**1**)

(b) (i) methane (**1**)

(ii) e.g. –45 (a negative number greater than –89) (**1**)

(iii) C_3H_8 (**1**)

2 (a)

(1)

(b)

(1)

(c)

H H H H H
| | | | |
H—C—C—C—C—C—H
| | | | |
H H H H H
(1)

3 C_4H_8 **(1)**

64. Properties of hydrocarbons

1 (a) $C_3H_8 + 5O_2 \rightarrow 3CO_2 + 4H_2O$ **(1)**

(b) propane **(1)**

2 (a) In tube A a colourless liquid **(1)** is formed. In tube B, the limewater changes from colourless **(1)** to cloudy **(1)**.

(b) Anhydrous copper sulfate **(1)** turns from white **(1)** to blue **(1)**.

(c) carbon dioxide **(1)** + water **(1)**

3 (a) octane **(1)**; it has a larger molecular size **(1)**

(b) pentane **(1)**

(c) It flows easily **(1)** and catches fire easily **(1)**.

65. Cracking

1 thermal decomposition **(1)**

2 (a) breaking up a large molecule to produce a smaller, more useful molecule **(2)**

(b) $C_8H_{18} \rightarrow C_6H_{14} + C_2H_4$ **(1)**

(c) catalytic **(1)** steam **(1)**

(d) Smaller hydrocarbons make better fuels than larger ones. **(1)** Alkenes can be used to make polymers. **(1)**

3 (a) bitumen and residue **(1)**

(b) B **(1)**

66. Alkenes

1

H H H
| | |
H—C—C=C
| |
H H
(1)

2 (a) B and D **(1)**

(b) C: propane **(1)** D: ethene **(1)**

(c) All contain hydrogen and carbon **(1)** only **(1)**.

(d) $CH_4 + 2O_2 \rightarrow CO_2 + 2H_2O$ **(2)**

(e) C_nH_{2n} **(1)**

3 (a) $x = 4$ **(1)** $y = 8$ **(1)**

(b) butene **(1)**

(c) one from:

H H
| |
H—C—C=C—C—H
| | | |
H H H H
(1)

H H H
| | |
H—C—C—C=C
| | |
H H H H
(1)

67. Reactions of alkenes

1 ethene **(1)**

2 (a) C=C **(1)**

(b) carbon dioxide **(1)** water **(1)**

(c) carbon monoxide **(1)** water **(1)**

(d) hydrogen **(1)**

(e) ethane **(1)**

(f) A and C **(1)**

(g) B and C **(1)**

3 (a) bromine water **(1)**

(b) alkane, bromine water stays orange in alkane **(1)**; alkene, orange to colourless in alkene **(1)**

68. Alcohols

1

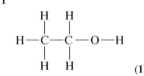

H H
| |
H—C—C—O—H
| |
H H
(1)

2 (a) OH/hydroxyl **(1)**

(b) any from: C_4H_9OH **(1)** $C_4H_{10}O$ **(1)**

3 (a) carbon dioxide **(1)** water **(1)**

(b) Butanol could be used as a solvent **(1)** or as a fuel **(1)**.

4

H H H
| | |
H—C—C—C—O—H
| | |
H H H
(1)

5 any three from: yeast **(1)** warm temperature **(1)** aqueous solution **(1)** no air **(1)**

69. Carboxylic acids

1

H H
| |
H—C—C=O
| |
H O—H
(1)

2 (a) circle the COOH **(1)**

(b) methanoic acid **(1)**

(c) HCOOH or H_2CO_2 **(1)**

(d) yes **(1)**

3 (a) butanol **(1)**

(b) carbon dioxide **(1)**

(c) Carboxylic acids react with alcohols **(1)**, forming an ester **(1)**.

70. Polymers

1 chloroethene **(1)**

2 (a) ethene **(1)** poly(ethene) **(1)**

(b) Polymers are long chain molecules **(1)** made by joining many monomers in a polymerisation reaction **(1)**.

3 (a) ethene **(1)**

(b) poly(ethene) **(1)**

(c) addition **(1)** polymerisation **(1)**

71. DNA

1 protein (1) starch (1)

2 (a) deoxyribonucleic acid (1)

(b) encodes genetic instructions (1) for the development and functioning of living organisms and viruses

(c) double helix (1)

(d) (i) 2 (1)

(ii) 4 (1)

3 (a) glucose (1)

(b) starch (1)

72. Extended response – Organic chemistry

Answer could include the following points. (6)

- yeast
- sugar
- produce carbon dioxide and ethanol
- warm temperature
- no air
- in aqueous solution
- Heat the dilute ethanol.
- Use antibumping granules for even boiling.
- The ethanol boils first and evaporates and moves into the condenser.
- Vapour cools and condenses and is collected.

This indicative content is not exhaustive; other creditworthy responses will be awarded marks too.

73. Pure substances and formulations

1 A pure substance in chemistry is a single element or compound (1). A pure substance in everyday life is one that has had nothing added to it (1).

2 determine its melting point (1)

3 steel (1)

4 (a) A solid (1) B solid (1) C liquid (1)

(b) A, element – sharp melting point and boiling point (1)

B, formulation – melting and boiling point is not sharp but has a range (1)

C, element – sharp melting point and boiling point (1)

5 Compare to the measured melting point in a data book (1).

74. Core practical – Chromatography

1 (a) A, purple food dye (1) B, filter paper/ chromatography paper (1) C, beaker (1) D, solvent (1)

(b) The paper is not touching the solvent (1), so the solvent cannot move up the paper and over the dye to separate it (1).

2 (a) 1 (1)

(b) Graphite in pencil does not dissolve in the solvent. (1)

(c) No, it has more than one spot on chromatogram. (1)

(d) distance moved by dye X = 0.6 cm (1)

distance moved by solvent = 1.0 cm (1)

$R_f = 0.6/1.0$ (1) = 0.6 (1)

75. Tests for gases

1 put a piece of damp litmus paper into the gas (1)

2 oxygen (1)

3 (a) calcium carbonate + hydrochloric acid → calcium chloride + water + carbon dioxide (1)

(b) colourless solution (1) to milky (1)

(c) calcium hydroxide solution (1) $Ca(OH)_2$ (1)

76. Tests for cations

1 copper(II) ion (1)

2 iron(II) sulfate solution (1)

3 (a) Dip a flame test wire loop in acid then heat in a Bunsen flame until there is no colour. (1)

Dip the loop in acid again and then into the compound. (1)

Hold the loop in the Bunsen flame and record colour. (1)

(b) Ionic substances contain two ions (1) and both ions must be identified (1).

(c) carbon dioxide (1)

(d) calcium carbonate (1)

4 (a) precipitation (1)

(b) Cu^{2+} (aq)

green

brown (3)

77. Tests for anions

1 potassium chloride (1)

2 First add hydrochloric acid. If carbonate ions are present a gas is produced that will turn limewater cloudy (1). To test for sulfate ions add barium chloride solution and a white precipitate results (1).

3 (a) Dissolve each solid in distilled water (1). Make up a solution of silver nitrate by adding silver nitrate solid to nitric acid solution. Add a few drops of silver nitrate solution (1). A white precipitate indicates chloride; a cream precipitate indicates bromide (1).

(b) Dissolve each solid in distilled water (1). Make up a solution of silver nitrate by adding silver nitrate solid to nitric acid solution. Add a few drops of silver nitrate solution (1). A white precipitate indicates chloride (1). Make up a solution of barium chloride by adding barium chloride solid to distilled water (1). Add a few drops of barium chloride solution. A white precipitate indicates chloride (1).

78. Flame emission spectroscopy

1 carrying out flame emission spectroscopy (1)

2 (a) calcium and copper ions (2)

(b) The sample is put into a flame (1) and the light given out is passed through a spectroscope (1). The output is a line spectrum that can be analysed to identify the metal ions (1).

(c) any two from: accurate (1) sensitive (1) can be used with small samples (1) rapid (1)

(d) 2,8,8 (1)

79. Core practical – Identifying a compound

1 (a) Add a spatula of the solid to water (1); stir to dissolve (1).

(b) sodium hydroxide (1)

(c) silver nitrate (1)

2 (a) sodium ions (1)

(b) aluminium ions (1)

(c) I⁻ (1)

(d) one from: aluminium iodide (1) sodium iodide (1)

80. Extended response – Chemical analysis

Answer could include the following points. (6)

Magnesium sulphate solution

- Add sodium hydroxide solution – forms a white precipitate, which does not dissolve on adding excess NaOH.
- Add barium chloride solution – forms a white precipitate.

Sodium chloride solution
- Flame test – gives a yellow flame.
- Add nitric acid and silver nitrate solution – forms a white precipitate.

Iron(II) iodide solution
- Add sodium hydroxide solution – forms a green precipitate, which does not dissolve on adding excess NaOH.
- Add nitric acid and silver nitrate solution – forms a yellow precipitate.

Magnesium bromide solution
- Add sodium hydroxide solution – forms a white precipitate, which does not dissolve on adding excess NaOH.
- Add nitric acid and silver nitrate – forms a cream precipitate.

This content is not exhaustive; other creditworthy responses will be awarded marks too.

81. The early atmosphere and today's atmosphere

1 nitrogen (**1**)

2 (a) oxygen 20 (**1**) nitrogen 78 (**1**)

(b) argon (**1**)

(c) methane (**1**) ammonia (**1**)

3 (a) $2Mg + O_2$ (**1**) $\rightarrow 2MgO$ (**1**)

(b) volume of oxygen = 28 cm^3 (**1**)

(c) $28/200 \times 100$ (**1**) = 14% (**1**)

82. Evolution of the atmosphere

1 (a) any three from:
- The early atmosphere contained no oxygen but today's atmosphere contains 20% oxygen. (**1**)
- The early atmosphere was mainly carbon dioxide (95.5%) but today's only has 0.04% carbon dioxide. (**1**)
- The early atmosphere had only 3.1% nitrogen but today's has 78%. (**1**)
- The earth's atmosphere today has slightly less argon (0.9%) compared to 1.2%. (**1**)

(b) We have accurate methods of measuring including instrumental methods. (**1**)

(c) Algae and plants decreased the percentage of carbon dioxide in the atmosphere by photosynthesis (**1**) and oxygen increased (**1**).

2 (a) $CO_2(g)$ (**1**)

(b) (i) shells (**1**)

(ii) limestone (**1**)

(c) $6CO_2 + 6H_2O \rightarrow C_6H_{12}O_6 + 6O_2$ (**1**)

83. Greenhouse gases

1 oxygen (**1**)

2 (a) 40% (**1**)

(b) water vapour (**1**), which has formula H_2O (**1**), and methane (**1**), which has formula CH_4 (**1**)

(c) any two from: The percentage of carbon dioxide decreased rapidly from 4500 to 3500 million years ago. (**1**)

The percentage of carbon decreased more gradually from 2500 years ago. (**1**)

The percentage of carbon dioxide levels off/stays constant. (**1**)

(d) combustion of fossil fuels (**1**) deforestation (**1**)

84. Global climate change

1 (a) During photosynthesis plants take in carbon dioxide (**1**) and give out oxygen (**1**).

(b) Burning fossil fuels (**1**) releases carbon dioxide (**1**) into the atmosphere.

(c) any two from:
- sea level rise, which may cause flooding and increased coastal erosion (**1**)
- more frequent and severe storms (**1**)
- changes in the amount, timing and distribution of rainfall (**1**)
- temperature and water stress for humans and wildlife (**1**)
- changes in the food-producing capacity of some regions (**1**)
- changes to the distribution of wildlife species. (**1**)

2 (a) When the carbon dioxide concentration increased (**1**) the temperature change increased (**1**).

(b) ice caps melting (**1**)

(c) an increase in the average global temperature (**1**)

85. Carbon footprint

1 the total amount of all greenhouse gases emitted over the full life cycle of a substance (**1**)

2 (a) 12% approx. (**1**)

(b) 28 + 12 + 3 = 43% approx. (**1**)

(c) any two from: use a bike (**1**) car share (**1**) use public transport (**1**) holiday locally (**1**)

(d) any two from: solar power (**1**) hydroelectric (**1**) geothermal (**1**) windpower (**1**)

(e) carbon dioxide (**1**) methane (**1**)

86. Atmospheric pollution

1 (a) 66 + 18 + 10 = 94 (**1**)

100 − 94 = 6% (**1**)

(b) sulfur dioxide (**1**)

2 (a) carbon monoxide and soot (**1**)

(b) carbon – global dimming (**1**)

carbon monoxide – prevents the blood from taking up oxygen (**1**)

carbon dioxide – global warming (**1**)

3 (a)

Name of pollutant	Formula	Effect of pollutant
sulfur dioxide	SO_2	acid rain/ respiratory problems
carbon monoxide	CO	toxic – can cause suffocation
soot/carbon particles/ particulates	C	global dimming/ health problems
nitrogen oxides	NOx	acid rain/ respiratory problems

(5)

(b) Sulfur in the fuel reacts with oxygen when it burns. (**1**)

Answers

(c) Carbon monoxide is produced by incomplete combustion of the fuel. (**1**)

87. Extended response – The atmosphere

Answer could include the following points. (**6**)

- The concentration of carbon dioxide changed little up until about 1800.
- The concentration of carbon dioxide increased dramatically from 1800 to 2000.
- This increase could be due to increased human activity such as
- increased combustion of fossil fuels
- and deforestation.
- Many scientists believe that increased carbon dioxide will cause the temperature of the Earth's atmosphere to increase at the surface.
- This will result in global climate change
- which may cause sea levels to rise and ice caps to melt – flooding.

This content is not exhaustive; other creditworthy responses will be awarded marks too.

88. The Earth's resources

1 renewable (**1**)
2 oil (**1**)
3 renewable (**1**) finite (**1**) renewable (**1**) renewable (**1**) finite (**1**)
4 Wool is natural. (**1**)
   Plastic is synthetic. (**1**)
   Cotton is natural. (**1**)
   Wood is natural. (**1**)

89. Water

1 (a) It contains dissolved minerals. (**1**)
   (b) step 1: passing through a filter bed (**1**) to remove any solids (**1**)
   step 2: sterilising using chlorine or ozone (**1**) to kill microbes (**1**)
   (c) (i) removal of salt from water (**1**)
       (ii) distillation (**1**) reverse osmosis (**1**)
       (iii) It requires large amounts of energy. (**1**)
2 (a) 1, screening and grit removal
       2, sedimentation
       3, anaerobic digestion of sewage sludge (**1**)
   (b) It removes large solids and grit from the waste water. (**1**)

90. Core practical – Analysis and purification of water

1 (a) in the conical flask (**1**)
   (b) in the test tube (**1**)
   (c) to cool the vapour and cause condensation (**1**)
   (d) A, conical flask; B, delivery tube (**1**)
   (e) Liebig condenser (**1**)
   (f) Measure its boiling point (**1**); it should be 100 °C (**1**).
   (g) Add barium chloride solution. (**1**)
   (h) It needs large amounts of energy and often this uses up finite resources (e.g., crude oil) (**1**); using fossil fuels to provide energy causes carbon dioxide and other pollutants to be released, which can lead to global warming or acid rain (**1**).

91. Life cycle assessment

1 An LCA can be carried out to assess the total impact on the environment of a product over its whole life, from extracting the raw materials to its disposal. (**2**)
2 (a) 7 520 000 (J) (**1**)
   (b) any three from:
       - extracting and processing raw materials (**1**)
       - manufacturing and packaging (**1**)
       - use and operation during its lifetime (**1**)
       - disposal at the end of its useful life, including transport and distribution at each stage (**1**)
   (c) To manufacture once, and fill the glass bottle four times, the energy is 7 520 000 + (2 000 000 × 4) = 15 520 000 joules (**2**)
       To manufacture four plastic bottles the energy is (4 × manufacture) + (4 × filling) = (4 × 2 200 000) + (4 × 4 500 000) = 26 800 000 J (**2**)
       Energy saving = 26 800 000 – 15 520 000 = 11 280 000 J (**1**)
   (d) any two from:
       - increased use of alternative energy supplies to manufacture the bottle (**1**)
       - energy conservation (**1**)
       - carbon capture and storage (**1**)
       - carbon off-setting, including through tree planting (**1**)

92. Conserving resources

1 (a) lead and aluminium (**1**)
   (b) because its ore might be scarce (**1**)
       because it might be expensive to extract the metal (**1**)
   (c) 72% of lead is recycled.
       72/100 × 4.6 = 3.312 = 3.3 million tonnes (**2**)
   (d) reduces the use of limited resources (**1**)
       reduces energy consumption (**1**)
       reduces waste (**1**)
2 (a) (2 × 27) + (3 × 16) = 102 (**1**)
   (b) (27 × 2)/102 ×100 = 52.9% (**2**)
   (c) any two from: it reduces the use of resources of bauxite (**1**) it causes much less energy consumption (**1**) reduces waste and the associated environmental impacts (**1**)

93. Corrosion

1 (a) Corrosion is the destruction of materials by chemical reactions with substances in the environment. (**1**)
   (b) air (**1**) water (**1**)
   (c) any two from: greasing (**1**) painting (**1**) electroplating (**1**)
2 (a) any two from: same volume of water (**1**) same temperature (**1**) identical nails (**1**) same mass of metal (**1**) same surface area of metal (**1**)
   (b) Copper and silver are less reactive than iron (**1**) so the nail acts sacrificially (**1**).
   (c) The nail would not have rusted in test tube 2 because zinc is more reactive than iron (**1**). The zinc and magnesium are more reactive than iron and so corrode instead of iron (**1**).
   (d) same results (**1**)

94. Alloys

1 (a) one from: a mixture of metals (**1**) a mixture of metals and non-metals (**1**)
   (b) metallic (**1**)

(c) There are different sized atoms (**1**) and so the layers of atoms do not slide easily over each other (**1**).

2 (a) (i) 18/24 × 100 = 75% (**2**)

(ii) number of carats = 24 × $\frac{50}{100}$ (**1**)
= 12 carats (**1**)

(b) copper and zinc, instruments/door fittings/water taps (**1**)

copper and tin, statues/decorative objects (**1**)

iron and carbon, cutting tools (**1**)

95. Ceramics, polymers and composites

1 carbon fibre (**1**)

2 (a) Thermosoftening polymers soften and melt when heated (**1**), while thermosetting polymers do not soften or melt when heated (**1**).

(b) thermosetting (**1**), so they do not melt from the heat of the hob (**1**)

(c) Thermosoftening polymers contain long polymer chains which are not joined to each other. (**1**)

Thermosetting polymers contain long polymer chains joined by cross links. (**1**)

3 ceramic (**1**) ceramic (**1**) polymer (**1**) polymer (**1**) ceramic (**1**)

96. The Haber process

1 (a) air (**1**)

(b) methane (natural gas)/electrolysis of water (**1**)

(c) iron (**1**)

(d) $N_2(g) + 3H_2(g) \rightleftharpoons 2NH_3(g)$ (**2**)

(e) The reaction is reversible. (**1**)

(f) 450, 200 (**1**)

(g) to liquefy ammonia (**1**)

(h) They are recycled. (**1**)

97. Fertilisers

1 (a) A, ammonium phosphate (**1**)
B, ammonium sulfate (**1**)

(b) $NH_3 + HCl \rightarrow NH_4Cl$ (**1**)

(c) (i) 80 (**1**)

(ii) 14 × 2/80 (**1**) × 100 = 35% (**1**)

(d) (i) Fertilisers are formulations of various salts which are used to improve agricultural productivity. (**1**)

(ii) NPK fertilisers contain nitrogen, phosphorus and potassium. (**1**)

2 It is insoluble. (**1**)

98. Extended response – Using resources

Answer could include the following points. (**6**)

- nitrogen + hydrogen ⇌ ammonia
- $N_2 + 3H_2 \rightleftharpoons 2NH_3$
- The raw materials are nitrogen and hydrogen.
- source for the nitrogen – air
- source for the hydrogen, e.g. methane
- The gases are purified
- and passed over a catalyst of iron
- at a high temperature (about 450 °C)
- and at a high pressure (about 200 atmospheres).
- The reaction is reversible.
- On cooling, the ammonia liquefies and is removed.

- The remaining hydrogen and nitrogen are recycled.

This content is not exhaustive; other creditworthy responses will be awarded marks too.

Timed Test 1

1 (a)

Statement	Structure

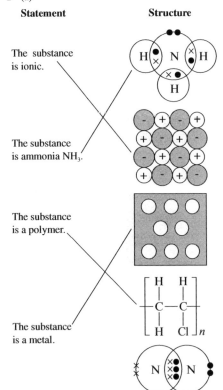

More than one line from each statement negates the mark. (**4**)

(b) carbon (**1**)

(c) It does not conduct electricity. (**1**)

(d) % = silicon atoms /total number of atoms × 100 = 14/28 (**1**) × 100 = 50% (**1**)

(e) methane (**1**)

(f) a mixture of a compound and two elements (**1**)

(g) filtration (**1**)

2 (a) type of metal (**1**)

(b) (i) balance (**1**) (ii) thermometer (**1**)

(c) magnesium sulfate + (**1**) copper (**1**)

(d) one from: blue solution fades/ turns colourless (**1**) brown/ orange deposit on magnesium (**1**)

(e) silver (**1**)

(f) magnesium, zinc, copper, silver (**2**); opposite way round (**1**)

(g) too reactive/too dangerous (**1**)

(h) any two from: same volume of copper sulfate (**1**) same concentration of copper sulfate (**1**) same mass of metal (**1**) same surface area of metal (**1**)

(i) iron (**1**)

(j) (i) $Fe_2O_3 + 2Al \rightarrow 2Fe + Al_2O_3$ (**1**)

(ii) Reduction is loss of oxygen (**1**); iron(III) oxide loses oxygen (**1**).

3 (a) (18.90 + 19.00)/2 (**1**) = 18.95 cm³ (**1**)

(b) burette (**1**)

(c) yellow to blue (**1**)

(d) any two from: add the sodium hydroxide solution in drops near the end point (**1**) swirl (**1**) use a pipette (**1**)

(e) 10 (**1**)

(f) pH probe (**1**)

4 (a) one from: bubbles (**1**) magnesium carbonate disappears (**1**)

(b)

Answer could include the following points. (**6**)

- sulfuric acid in beaker (or similar)
- Add magnesium carbonate one spatula at a time
- until magnesium carbonate is in excess or until no more effervescence occurs.
- Filter using filter paper and funnel.
- Filter off excess magnesium carbonate.
- Pour solution into evaporating basin/dish.
- Heat using Bunsen burner.
- Leave to cool and crystallise/leave for water to evaporate/boil off water.
- Decant solution.
- Pat dry (using filter paper).

(c) Wear safety spectacles/goggles. (**1**)

(d) % = 1.8/2.0 × 100 (**1**) = 90% (**1**)

(e) any one from: loss of product in transfer of apparatus (**1**) filtering (**1**) not all magnesium sulfate crystallises (**1**)

(f) total mass of reactants = 84 + 98 = 182 (**1**)

120/182 (**1**) × 100 = 65.9% (**1**)

5 (a) (i) metallic (**1**) (ii) covalent (**1**)

(b) • electrons transferred from magnesium to chlorine (**1**)
- Magnesium loses two electrons, one to each chlorine (**1**)
- forming Mg^{2+} (**1**).
- Each chlorine atom gains 1 electron (**1**)
- forming two Cl^- ions (**1**).

(c) shared pair between H and Cl (**1**); rest correct – no additional hydrogen electrons and 3 non-bonding pairs on chlorine (**1**)

(d) (i) Hydrogen chloride has a low melting point as it has weak intermolecular forces. (**1**)

(ii) Magnesium chloride conducts electricity when dissolved as the ions can move and carry charge. (**1**)

(e) hydrogen ion (**1**) chloride ion (**1**)

(f) 1×10^{-10} m (**1**)

6 (a) 28.0 (**1**)

(b) plotting points correctly (**2**); a smooth line (**1**)

(c) The temperature increases so heat is given out. (**1**)

(d) any one from: burette (**1**) measuring cylinder (**1**) syringe (**1**)

(e) any one from: heat loss (**1**) inaccurate volumes (**1**) use lid on beaker or insulate (**1**) use a pipette (**1**)

(f) HCl (**1**) H_2O (**1**)

7 (a) any one from: flame (**1**) smoke (**1**) energy given out (**1**)

(b) potassium hydroxide + hydrogen (**1**)

(c) Each potassium atom loses an electron to form a positive ion. (**1**)

(d) (i) white solid soluble in water (**1**)

(ii) cathode, potassium; anode, chlorine (**1**)

(e) (i) Bromine/lead are toxic. (**1**)

(ii) lamp/ammeter (**1**)

8 (a)

Answer could include the following points. (**6**)

Improvement on Newland's

- Mendeleev overcame some of the problems by leaving gaps for elements that he thought had not been discovered
- and in some places changed the order based on atomic weights.

Comparison to modern table

- Mendeleev listed elements in his periodic table by atomic mass but the modern periodic table lists by atomic number.
- In Mendeleev's periodic table there are no noble gases and no block of transition metals, but both are in the modern periodic table.
- In Mendeleev's periodic table there are spaces for undiscovered elements but in the modern periodic table there are no spaces.
- Mendeleev's periodic table has fewer elements than the modern periodic table.

(b) (i) most reactive in group 1, rubidium; most reactive in group 7, bromine (**1**)

(ii) chlorine (**1**)

(iii) The forces between argon atoms are stronger (**1**)

(iv) one from: iron (**1**) copper (**1**)

9 (a) (35 × (75.78/100)) (**1**) + (37 × (24.22/100)) (**1**)

26.52 + 8.96 (**1**) = 35.48 (**1**)

(b) (i) 11 protons (**1**) 12 neutrons (**1**) 11 electrons (**1**)

(ii) 2,8,1 (**1**)

(iii) NaCl (**1**)

(c) 213 (**2**); allow (**1**) for evidence of 27 + 3(14 + (3 × 16))

Timed Test 2

1 (a) It has a sharp melting point. (**1**)

(b) glass (**1**)

(c) air (**1**) paint (**1**)

(d) reverse osmosis (**1**)

(e) recognisable apparatus with labels: evaporating basin containing 50 cm^3 of sodium chloride solution (**1**) Bunsen burner (**1**) tripod and gauze (**1**)

(f) (i) total mass = 37.5 g (**1**)

15.0 = 15/37.5 × 100 (**1**) = 40% (**1**)

(ii) They have atoms of different sizes in their structures. (**1**)

2 (a) potassium (**1**) iron(II) (**1**) chloride (**1**)

(b) The gas produced would be carbon dioxide. The test for this is to use limewater (**1**), which turns cloudy in the presence of carbon dioxide (**1**).

3 (a) Bunsen burner (**1**)

(b) It may contain some air. (**1**)

(c) to catalyse the reaction (**1**)

(d) In alkene only bromine water changes (**1**) from orange to colourless (**1**).

(e) (i) C_6H_{12} (**1**)

(ii) It contains carbon and hydrogen (**1**) only (**1**).

(iii) steam/water (**1**)

(iv)
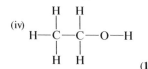
(**1**)

(v) $2CO_2$ (**1**) + $3H_2O$ (**1**)

(vi) C_2H_6O (**1**)

4 (a) so the line does not run /dissolve (**1**)

(b) blue (**1**)

(c) red (**1**)

(d) green (**1**)

(e)

	Distance in mm
Distance moved by green ink	35 (**1**)
Distance moved from start line to solvent front	80 (**1**)

R_f = 35/80 (**1**) = 0.4375 (**1**) = 0.44 (**1**)

5 (a) gas syringe (**1**)

(b) Mg(s) (**1**) H_2(g) (**1**)

(c) advantage – any one from: convenient (**1**) easy (**1**) quick to use (**1**)

disadvantage – reference to inaccurate measurement (**1**)

(d) sensible scales, using at least half the grid for the points (**1**)

all points correct (**1**)

best fit line (**1**)

(e) 71–73 s – read from graph (**1**)

(f) volume of gas = 17 (**1**) cm^3 read from graph

mean rate = 17/45= 0.377 (**1**) cm^3/s

0.4 to 1 significant figure (**1**)

(g) There are more particles in the same volume (**1**). There are more collisions with the activation energy (**1**).

(h) any one from: pipette/burette to measure out the acid (**1**) repeat and take average (**1**) take more frequent readings (**1**) suitable method for reducing initial loss of gas (**1**)

(i) Place the conical flask with the acid and magnesium on the balance (**1**) and record the mass every 30 seconds (**1**).

6 (a) N_2 + $3H_2$ ⇌ $2NH_3$ (**1**)

(b) The reaction is reversible. (**1**)

(c) iron (**1**)

(d) temperature, 450°C; pressure, 200 atm (**1**)

(e) As temperature increases yield decreases. (**1**)

(f) (i) Between 1960 and 2000 the consumption of nitrogen fertilisers increases. (**1**)

(ii) from graph: 10 megatonnes (**1**) 1×10^7 tonnes (**1**)

(g) nitrogen (**1**) phosphorus (**1**) potassium (**1**)

(h) (i) Adding fertiliser increases the height of the plant (**1**); use of data, e.g. with no fertiliser the average height is 12 cm but when fertiliser is added the heights are at least 15 cm (**1**).

(ii) ammonium nitrate (**1**)

(iii) $(NH_4)_3PO_4$ (**1**)

(iv) nitric acid (**1**)

7 (a)

Answer could include the following points. (**6**)

- carbon monoxide produced by incomplete combustion
- soot (carbon particles) produced by incomplete combustion
- sulfur dioxide produced by sulfur when sulfur impurities burn
- oxides of nitrogen formed when nitrogen from the air reacts with oxygen at the hot temperature produced by the burning fuel
- unburnt hydrocarbons
- carbon dioxide produced when fuel burns
- Carbon monoxide is a toxic gas.
- Carbon monoxide is colourless and odourless and so is not easily detected.
- Sulfur dioxide and oxides of nitrogen are acidic and dissolve to form acid rain.
- Sulfur dioxide and oxides of nitrogen cause respiratory problems in humans.
- Particulates cause global dimming.
- Particulates cause health problems for humans.
- Carbon dioxide causes global warming. (**6**)

(b) methane (**1**)

(c) The carbon footprint is the total amount of carbon dioxide and other greenhouse gases (**1**) emitted over the full life cycle of a product, service or event (**1**).

(d) methane (**1**) carbon dioxide (**1**)

8 (a) N_2 (**1**)

(b) Algae evolved (**1**) and plants produced oxygen by photosynthesis (**1**).

(c) (i) $2Cu + O_2 \rightarrow 2CuO$ (**2**)

(ii) The gas must be at room temperature when its volume is measured (**1**)

(iii) volume decrease = 32 – 24 = 8 (**1**)

% decrease = 8/32 (**1**) = 25% (**1**)

(iv) The result is higher than the percentage of oxygen in today's atmosphere (**1**) there may still be oxygen in the apparatus which did not react (**1**).

9 *Answer could include the following points.* (**6**)

- named container – test tubes /beaker
- Leave for 1 week.
- iron nail in water
- Water contains dissolved air and water.
- iron nail in boiled water and layer of oil
- Boiled water contains no air.
- layer of oil keeps out oil
- iron nail in test tube with anhydrous calcium chloride/drying agent and stoppered
- Anhydrous calcium chloride removes water.

Notes

Notes

Published by Pearson Education Limited, 80 Strand, London, WC2R 0RL.

www.pearsonschoolsandfecolleges.co.uk

Text © Pearson Education Limited 2017
Typeset and produced by Phoenix Photosetting
Illustrations © Pearson
Cover illustration by Miriam Sturdee

The right of Nora Henry to be identified as author of this work has been
asserted by her in accordance with the Copyright, Designs and Patents Act
1988.

First published 2017

20 19 18 17
10 9 8 7 6 5 4 3 2 1

British Library Cataloguing in Publication Data
A catalogue record for this book is available from the British Library

ISBN 978 1 292 13123 8

Content written by Iain Brand and Nigel Saunders has been included in this
book.

The publisher would like to thank the following for their kind permission to
reproduce their photographs:

Pearson Education Ltd: Trevor Clifford 105

Printed in Slovakia by Neografia

Printed in Great Britain
by Amazon